FROM KITE TO KITTY HAWK

by Richard W. Bishop

ILLUSTRATED BY JOHN TEPPICH

FROM KITE TO KITTY HAWK

THOMAS Y. CROWELL COMPANY
NEW YORK

3428

629.1
Bis

Manufactured in the United States of America by The Vail-Ballou Press, Inc., Binghamton, N.Y.

Library of Congress Catalog Card No. 58-6603

Ninth Printing

To my three favorite fans,
Dick, Greg, and Jill, this book
is respectfully dedicated

ACKNOWLEDGMENTS

The author wishes to acknowledge the following sources for brief quotations. The pages on which the quotations appear in this book are given in parenthesis.

Conquest of the Air, by Laurance Yard Smith; Frederick A. Stokes Company, New York, 1919 (page 49).

Everyman's Book of Flying, by Orville H. Kneen; Frederick A. Stokes Company, New York, 1930 (page 117).

Historic Airships, by Rupert Sargent Holland; Macrae Smith Company, Philadelphia, 1928 (pages 144–145).

Horizons Unlimited, by S. Paul Johnston; Duell, Sloan & Pearce, 1941 (pages 134, 174).

Man's Fight to Fly, by John P. V. Heinmuller; Funk & Wagnalls Company, New York, 1944 (page 151).

Metamorphoses, by Ovid (page 6).

Mind of Leonardo da Vinci, by Edward McCurdy; Dodd, Mead & Company, 1948 (page 118).

Romance of Aeronautics, The, by Charles C. Turner; J. B. Lippincott Company, London, 1912 (pages 79–80, 88, 102).

Romance of the Airmen, by Pauline A. Humphries and Gertrude Hosey; Ginn and Company, Boston, 1931 (pages 72–73).

Sky High, The Story of Aviation, by Eric Hodgins and F. Alexander Magoun; Little, Brown and Company, Boston, 1930 (pages 116, 141, 145).

Story of Aircraft, by Chelsea Fraser; Thomas Y. Crowell Company, New York, 1933, 1939 editions (pages 120, 150–151).

This Flying Game, by Brig. Gen. H. H. Arnold and Major Ira C. Eaker; Funk & Wagnalls Company, New York, 1956 (pages 23–24).

Preface

In 1903, at Kitty Hawk, Orville and Wilbur Wright made the first sustained flight in heavier-than-air craft propelled by its own engine. In the fifty-some years that followed, the airplane changed from a canvas-covered framework of spindling sticks to the sleek jet-engined bird of today. In 1903 the Wright plane flew 852 feet in fifty-nine seconds. Today multi-motored man-made eagles of the sky fly thousands of miles, sail off for many hours at a time and travel at speeds incomprehensible to men fifty years ago. Indeed, airplanes have now doubled the speed of sound and have climbed higher than seventy thousand feet.

From Kite to Kitty Hawk is the story of man's primitive desire to fly and what he did about it.

vii

Aviation is not really fifty years old. Aviation is thousands upon thousands of years old. It began not on the sands of Kitty Hawk but in the mind of man before the beginning of history, almost at the beginning of time.

In the story of man's struggle with the sky, we must begin in that legendary and nebulous half-world of myth. For every myth there is a fact, for every legend there is a deed. Can we say that the flight of Daedalus and Icarus is entirely false? May it not have its foundation with some man, somewhere, strapping feathered wings to his arms and trying to imitate the flying creatures of the world?

But the story of aviation is not all myth. Far from it. It is based mostly upon fact. The story of man's fulfillment of his desire to fly is based on many facts and on many deeds. Some of them are small and some are large. One hundred and fifty years before the birth of Christ, Hero discovered the fundamentals of jet propulsion, the same fundamentals which send our planes skimming through the sky at seventeen hundred miles per hour today. In 1496, four years after Columbus discovered America, Leonardo da Vinci designed the parachute and the rotating wing, and drew a picture of a workable aerial propeller.

Aviation developed in many ways. It is the story of kites in China and of boomerangs in Australia. Soap bubbles played an important part in man's struggle with the sky and so did rubber bands. When man first discovered that he had a great and burning desire to take to the air, there was only one way he could move and that was forward. Step by step he made his way in that direction; sometimes the steps were faltering and at other times his progress was marked by the strides of seven league boots.

This book is the story of these bits of progress from the beginning until man's ambition was fulfilled.

It may seem strange and unusual that the parachute was designed before man could fly. And yet, in a sense, it is not unusual at all. Certainly man must fall before he could float. With the development of the balloon, man thought he was flying. Actually he was floating. It was not until the glider was invented that man could really fly. Even then, he depended on gravity for his motor. Each of these steps was painful. Each required several smaller steps before the ultimate goal was reached. Sometimes the step was taken by accident, sometimes by design.

Sometimes brave men risked their lives, and sometimes they lost them, in order that the great goal might be reached. Not until the struggle was over was it possible to determine the value of each stepping stone in the path to flight.

It is to these brave pioneers that this book is respectfully dedicated.

RICHARD W. BISHOP

CONTENTS

Lighter than Air

The Parachute

Heavier than Air

Lighter than Air

1: EARLY MYTHS AND EARLY DREAMS

PANTING and trembling, the hunter flung himself into a thicket. He lay there motionless, hoping that the leather hides he wore for clothing blended well with the brown foliage.

He was frightened.

The crashing of the animal's heavy feet drew nearer, and then, to the man's great relief, passed by.

Only a few moments before he had been the hunter. Now, the breaking of his small and pitiful spear had quickly turned him into the hunted.

There was a flutter of wings, and a covey of birds took to the air. The hunter watched them enviously, wishing he, too, could fly away from the dangers that frightened him.

FROM KITE TO KITTY HAWK

It was at that moment that aviation was born.

It seems strange, in a way, to say that aviation did not begin with Orville and Wilbur Wright on the sands of Kitty Hawk in 1903. But it did not. Man fell and floated and flew long before then. And before that, he dreamed.

In the dim and distant past, prehistoric man in the pursuit of wild animals for food reached a river which he could not cross, a canyon over which he could not leap, or a barrier which he could not penetrate. For his transportation he relied upon his feet. There were no roads, and trees impeded his progress. There were no bridges, and if he could not swim or ford the river he must build a raft or float across on a log. His search for food and shelter was hindered by the obstacles of nature. More often than not, he was in danger.

It was at this time that man noticed the bird. It was then that he began to envy its easy conquest of the perils and obstacles which thwarted his desires and frustrated his ambitions. It was then that primitive man wished that he could fly. His wishes soon turned to dreams, and his dreams to myths and stories and legends. One of the earliest of these legends was the tale of Daedalus and Icarus.

In the reign of King Minos of Crete, there lived a skillful sculptor whose name was Daedalus. Minos was a cruel king, and his many cruelties made him many enemies. He was also somewhat of a coward. Since cowards must have a place to hide, Minos asked Daedalus to build him an endless labyrinth.

Daedalus built the labyrinth and it was truly a great work of art. Its passages twisted and turned upon each other in such a way that King Minos could skillfully dodge and hide from the worst of his enemies. It had neither beginning nor end. It wandered like the River Maeander, now turning upon itself, now doubling in the same direction. At first King Minos was pleased with the result of the endeavors of Daedalus, but his pleasure was short lived. Daedalus was too clever a man. The cowardly king reasoned that if Daedalus could build a labyrinth as well as he had done, he could outwit him.

So Minos shut the skillful Daedalus in a tower on the island of Crete. He placed guards about the tower but, not satisfied with these ordinary precautions, he also guarded the vessels that left the island.

Imprisoned with Daedalus was his son, Icarus, and Daedalus quickly set to scheming to obtain freedom for both of them. "Cruel Minos may control the earth and the water," Daedalus told himself, "but he cannot control the regions of the air." He set his cunning to new work and set his son, Icarus, to gathering feathers from the ledges of the palace.

The larger feathers he joined together with a strong thread, the smaller feathers he fastened with wax. The whole he molded together with a gentle curve like the wing of a bird, working them over with his skillful fingers to fashion two pairs of wings. When at last the work was completed he fastened them to his arms and to the arms of Icarus.

"My boy, take care to wing your course along the middle air," Daedalus told his son. "If low, the surges wet your flagging plumes; if high, the sun the melting wax consumes." Icarus nodded, and promised to follow his father's instructions.

At first Icarus kept his pledge and followed his father through the air from the tower to the edge of the island of Crete and out over the ocean beyond. Father and son mounted upward. Below, a mountain shepherd leaning on his crook stared at the miraculous sight, and a gaping plowman cried in startled surprise.

Through the azure sky the pair made their way, at first cautious and then with more confidence as they passed Samos and Delos behind them.

Daedalus, who was older, remained cautious. But Icarus, the son, became overconfident and aspired to loftier aims, which made him fly higher and higher toward the sky. Growing wild and wanton, the boy soared nearer and nearer to the sun. His nearness to the blazing orb softened the wax which held the feathers together. One by one they dropped from his wings until he began to fall.

Down to the sea he tumbled.

"Ho, Icarus! Where are you?" the father cried.

It was too late. The son plunged downward into the blue waters of the ocean and was lost to the memory of man. Sadly the father winged his way onward and arrived safe in Sicily where he built a temple to Apollo and there placed his wings as an offering to the god. But ever after he mourned the loss of his only son, Icarus, and named the blue waters the Icarian Sea in memory of his lost loved one.

The Greeks also told of Perseus who swooped down on the rocky shore to slay the sea monster and free the beautiful Andromeda. Mercury and Hermes were Greek gods who were able to fly.

7

FROM KITE TO KITTY HAWK

In China, there lived an emperor by the name of Shun, who was supposed to have used wings several times to escape from dangers more than two thousand years before Christ was born.

Alexander the Great was supposed to have flown in a chariot drawn by hungry birds. To make them fly, he dangled a bit of suet in front of them with a long pole and a piece of string.

Pegasus, the winged horse, had many adventures, as did the enchanted horse of the Arabian Nights. And when man ran short of other dreams there was always the magic carpet!

Man's dreams never stop. Soon after man learned to float through the air in balloons, Jules Verne's story *Five Weeks in a Balloon* captured the imagination of all of his readers. Even earlier, Edgar Allan Poe, in "The Unparalleled Adventure of One Hans Pfaall" realistically described a balloon trip which ended on another planet.

But in the meantime, while man was dreaming, he was also acting. He was trying. He was experimenting. Aviation was becoming more than a dream in the minds of men.

Step by step, it was becoming a reality.

2: THE GRAND OLD MAN

LEONARDO da Vinci pushed back his black cloth cap and rubbed his forehead with the back of his hand. He started to smooth his white beard, but stopped quickly as he noticed the oil paint that stained his fingers. Leaning back on his stool, he surveyed the painting that he had just completed. It was New Year's day, 1496.

The painting was done. Now that it was finished, Leonardo was not certain that it was to his liking. It reminded him of the work of Andrea Pisano with whom Leonardo did not always see eye to eye. Tomorrow, Leonardo thought, I must rework this painting until it suits me.

The thought of Pisano reminded Leonardo of the bas-relief on the campanile showing Daedalus trying out his

9

wings. Leonardo smiled. Poor Daedalus! It was fortunate for him that he was only a myth!

For thirty years Leonardo had been studying the flight of birds, watching them take off in flight from land and water, watching them soar, watching the frantic efforts of the hummingbird, watching the sea gull dive, watching all kinds of birds come to rest after an arduous flight. Already Leonardo's notebooks were crammed with jottings of his observations.

Now he was ready to experiment with a flying machine of his own.

At home that night, his paints and brushes safely stored away, Leonardo sat before a bare wood table, his great volumes of manuscripts spread out before him. There was the drawing of the parachute, constructed in the shape of a tent, the model of which had worked so well. The old gentleman remembered when it had been tested.

The latest of Leonardo's models resembled a bat. It was made of bamboo and pine and starched taffeta. Its flapping wings were operated by the hands and feet of the flyer.

It would be wise, Leonardo thought, if I were to try this flying machine over a lake, that I should strap a long leather bottle to my waist in the event that I should fall. The leather bottle would be a life preserver that would keep me from drowning and I would do myself no harm.

As the hour grew late, Leonardo wrote his last notation of the evening: "Tomorrow morning on the second of January, 1496, I will make the leather thongs for the straps and the trial." He entered the words carefully, with letters reversed, and from right to left in his customary "mirror style."

He sat back in his chair and tried to visualize what it would be like to fly. He could not know then that his model would never work because he lacked power. Man's arms and legs were not built to fly. Nor were they strong enough to flap man-made wings to keep him in the air. Perhaps if Leonardo had realized this, he would have been discouraged. But he should not have been. For Leonardo had brought aviation from the land of the dream to the land of experiment and reality. His parachute was the forerunner of the life-saving parachute of today. The construction of his model led to the fabric-covered airplane of early flight. His drawings of the airscrew propeller, which he likened to a thin ruler that was twirled overhead, presented man with the fundamental concept of the airplane propeller of today.

In his manuscript "On the Flight of Birds" there appeared, written in his peculiar right to left style, many rules that later were to guide those who followed him. If his single maxim: "An object offers as much resistance to the air as air does to the object," had been more closely observed, man might have overcome his struggle with the sky a hundred years earlier than he did.

Leonardo da Vinci is best known today as the painter of *Mona Lisa, The Last Supper,* and *La Belle Ferronnière.* But men of science know him also as a famous inventor. As military engineer under Cesare Borgia, he discovered and made known some of the earliest laws of hydraulics. He designed a canal which was not constructed until two hundred years after his death, when the plans were followed in every detail. His drawings for inventions include an automobile powered with a spring motor, a life belt, a camera, roller bearings, and the telescope. He was the first to show America and the Antarctic continents on maps. Even before Columbus discovered America, Leonardo not only agreed with Columbus that the earth was round, but estimated its diameter at seven thousand miles, only nine hundred miles from fact.

Leonardo proved that fossils are skeletons of animals instead of mineral formations as his contemporaries believed. He understood the circulation of the blood in the body, and discovered that the number of rings in a tree trunk indicated its age. He was the first to use the plus and minus sign in addition and subtraction. Leonardo also designed an armored tank and vanes for the controlled direction of bombs, and it was a drawing in his notebook for a steam cannon that provided James Watt with the basis of his idea for the steam engine.

Leonardo even invented the wheelbarrow.

The work of Leonardo da Vinci was of great value, not only in the field of aviation but in many other scientific endeavors as well.

But as Leonardo sat in his home, his manuscripts strewn about him, he did not know, he could not measure the tremendous stride that he had taken in the field of flight. It satisfied his great and fertile mind that he was curious, that he was interested, and his curiosity and his interest were reward enough for him.

Although Leonardo da Vinci had firmly planted the first real stepping stone in man's struggle to the sky, it remained for modern man to make a motor which could keep him in the air.

Here was a beginning of the conquest. It would not end until four hundred years later on another continent. When it did end, Leonardo da Vinci's words: "There shall be wings," were inscribed on the Wright Memorial at Kitty Hawk, North Carolina.

3: MAN FLOATS

I THINK we are ready for a public demonstration," Étienne Montgolfier told his younger brother Joseph.

"I am not so sure," Joseph rejoined. "People will never believe that we can make a paper bag float through the sky."

Étienne smiled. "It will be quite different from the little paper sack which we had floating about our kitchen," he agreed. "Do you remember how curious it seemed to us at first?"

Joseph nodded. "I remember only too well." His eyes had a faraway look. "It was almost a year ago that we heard Priestly's paper about the different kinds of air, when it was read at the Academy of Lyons," he said.

Étienne smiled again. "Do you remember too how we studied the clouds?"

"And Francesco Lana's copper spheres with the oars and the sails to make them go?" Joseph laughed.

"That was no worse than Joseph Galien's theory of moving one hundred million cubic feet of mountain air into a valley to use in lifting his ship . . ."

". . . and when he found he could not carry the air down the mountain side in his pocket," Joseph agreed, "he left the problem of carrying the rarefied air to experienced engineers."

The brothers became serious once more.

"I think it was Tiberius Cavallo, the Italian, who gave us the real idea," Étienne broke the silence. "His treatise on soap bubbles filled with hydrogen gas gave us the idea of trying it in paper bags. Inflammable air, I think he called it."

"Yes, but it didn't work. The inflammable air was all right for soap bubbles, but it was too thin for paper and escaped through its pores. I think it was watching the smoke rise from the kitchen stove that really helped the most."

"Maybe," his brother nodded. "But how about our good neighbor who came running when she saw the smoke blowing out the windows when our paper bag tipped over near the ceiling? It was her idea that we tie the pan holding the fire underneath the bag to keep it upright!"

"That's true."

There was another silence. "Do you really think . . ." both brothers began at once.

They both laughed again. Then Étienne said: "Yes, I think we are ready for a public demonstration. We must show the public our discovery and bear the brunt of their laughter and ridicule if we fail."

On June 5, 1783, the Montgolfier brothers were prepared. As paper manufacturers, they had reluctantly discarded the bag made of paper alone, and had constructed a huge linen sphere, lined with paper, thirty-five feet in diameter and weighing three hundred pounds. Their announcement of the public demonstration had aroused great curiosity among the people of Annonay, in Auvergne, France. Invitations had been sent to the state assembly of Vivarais which was then in session, and a huge gathering had braved the blistering hot afternoon sun in the market place. In the center of the throng the great linen ball hung limply. Joseph and Étienne Montgolfier were beside the bag, stuffing straw into the container below it and attending to the countless details necessary to inflate the huge paper and linen bag to a circumference of more than one hundred feet.

Joseph cast a nervous glance over his shoulder. He could see that the crowd was restless, that people were nudging each other. He was afraid that they had come to ridicule the discovery.

"Suppose it shouldn't work?" Joseph asked his brother.

Blairsville Junior High School
Blairsville, Pennsylvania

"It will work," Étienne said confidently.

Joseph drew a deep breath, looked toward the clear blue sky overhead, and touched his torch to the bundle of chopped straw fastened beneath the bag. A small flame licked at the dry straw and grew larger. Soon the fire was blazing and smoking.

Nothing happened. A murmur went up from the crowd, grew in proportion, and turned into a thunderous sound. Joseph watched the fire intently. The straw crackled, the smoke began to fill the linen bag. Little by little the bag grew in size and changed from a limp and lifeless thing to a strong and buoyant ship of the air that was determined to break its bounds.

The roar of the crowd died once more to a murmur. As the huge bag began to tug at the ropes that held it, there was a burst of applause and a cheer. Ten minutes had passed. The balloon was full! Slowly it began to rise! It was going to fly!

The ropes were released. Up and up the balloon soared, the wind carrying it over Annonay. As one body, the crowd began to run, following the gigantic ship of the air.

For ten minutes or more the balloon continued to climb. How high was it? How high was up? One thousand, two thousand, three thousand feet? Some spectators believed it was as high as six!

The balloon was becoming a speck in the sky and could barely be seen by the running crowd below. Then, as the fires died out and the air in the big sphere cooled, it began its slow descent.

A mile and a half away from the market place the people of Annonay came upon the balloon. The frightened farmers in whose field it had landed had made short work of it with pitchforks and flails.

But Étienne and Joseph Montgolfier did not mind. The crowd that had come to laugh and jeer at them had remained to cheer. Those who had come to ridicule the young paper manufacturers were now slapping them on the back and congratulating them. In place of the ridicule which the crowd had been ready to heap upon them, the Montgolfier brothers were being treated with respect.

The huge linen bag was called a "montgolfier" in honor of its discoverers and it was not until some time later that it became known as a balloon.

With the Montgolfier brothers man had taken another great stride forward in his struggle toward the sky.

4: COMMAND PERFORMANCE

BENJAMIN FRANKLIN was enjoying his visit to France. He meant to see all of the sights while he was there and it was his special wish to see the new montgolfier that was attracting so much attention among the French people.

It was September 19, 1783. The Montgolfiers, after their most successful experiment at Annonay, France, had been invited by Louis XVI and his queen, Marie Antoinette, to demonstrate their new discovery to the royal family and their guests.

Already Étienne Montgolfier had lectured at the Royal Academy of Science and had repeated his balloon demonstrations for the members. Already the Montgolfier brothers had constructed larger and more powerful balloons and together they were the heroes of the nation.

Now the command performance was to begin. The new montgolfier was a beautiful thing, Benjamin Franklin thought. It was blue in color and the signs of the zodiac were painted on its side. The royal coat of arms appeared as well, inscribed in gold.

The montgolfier rested on a wooden platform and under the opening at the base, which was some fifteen feet across, there hung a wicker basket.

Benjamin Franklin turned to a friend who stood beside him. "What can the basket be for?" he asked.

"Haven't you heard?" the friend replied. "They are going to send some animals up in the montgolfier."

"Animals?"

"Yes. A sheep, a rooster, and a duck."

Benjamin Franklin pursed his lips. For a moment he was startled. Then he said: "Will it do them no harm?"

The other shrugged. "Some say they will freeze."

"Birds do not freeze," Benjamin Franklin observed.

"Others say they will not be able to breathe."

"Birds can breathe." Benjamin Franklin looked once more at the huge balloon that was filling rapidly with the smoke from the flames below. "I think the animals will be all right."

The royal family was watching the proceedings intently. Franklin could see their earnest gaze upon the Montgolfier brothers and upon their assistants who were now holding fast to the rope leashes fastened to the montgolfier.

In a moment it would be one o'clock, the time for the scheduled flight. Franklin watched the Montgolfier brothers place the sheep and the rooster and the duck, in small cages, in the wicker basket beneath the tugging linen bag.

At exactly one o'clock the ropes were cut away. The balloon began to climb. There was a gasp from the crowd, but otherwise all was quiet. The heads of the royal guards tipped upward watching the montgolfier in flight. The balloon continued to climb, and with it the sheep, the rooster, and the duck. It was impossible to say how high the montgolfier went; there was no way to measure its distance. Some thought it soared to a height of fifteen hundred feet, others placed its ascent at thirteen thousand. But certain it was that the balloon with its animal passengers flew for eight minutes and came to rest in Vaucresson Wood, two miles away. There it was set upon by frightened peasants once more and destroyed.

That night both Louis XVI and Benjamin Franklin were busy with their quill pens.

Louis XVI was concerned. His people were afraid of this amazing new discovery. He was writing a proclamation. It read: "A discovery has been made which the government deems as right to make known so that alarm may not be occasioned to the people. On calculating the different weights

of inflammable and common air it has been found that a balloon filled with inflammable air will rise toward heaven till it is in equilibrium with the surrounding air; which may not happen till it has attained to a great height. Anyone who should see such a globe, resembling the moon in an eclipse, should be aware that far from being an alarming phenomenon it is only a machine made of taffetas or light canvas covered with paper, that cannot possibly cause any harm and which will some day prove serviceable to the wants of society."

Benjamin Franklin's thoughts were turned in another direction. He was writing in his notebook. "Among the pleasantries that conversation produces on this subject, some suppose flying to be now invented, and that since men may be supported in the air, nothing is wanted but some light handy instruments to steer and direct motion. Some think progressive motion on the earth may be advanced by it and that a running footman or a horse hung or suspended under such a globe so as to have no more weight pressing the earth with his feet than perhaps eight or ten pounds, might with a fair wind run in a straight line across countries as fast as that wind, and over hedges, ditches, and even water. It has been fancied that in time people will keep such globes anchored in the air, to which by pulleys they may draw up game to be preserved in the cool and water to be frozen when ice is wanted. And that to get money, it will be contrived to give people an extensive view of the country by running them up in an elbow chair a mile high for a guinea."

It was while Benjamin Franklin was penning these thoughts that a friend came to him and asked: "But what of the sheep, the rooster, and the duck? Did they perish?"

"Perish?" asked Benjamin Franklin with a smile. "Perish? No, they did not perish. They landed without the loss of a single bit of wool or a single feather."

5: MAN TAKES TO THE SKIES

THE Marquis d'Arlandes leaned against the edge of the basket fastened beneath a huge montgolfier and looked skyward. The wind was from the northwest and the sky had partially filled with clouds. But it was a gentle wind, and the linen bag above them swayed slightly with the breeze tugging at the cords that held it down.

"Do you think we should try it today?" the marquis asked his companion, Jean François de Pilâtre de Rozier.

De Rozier looked at his friend and grinned. "And why not?" he asked. "The breeze is gentle and there are eight strong men with ropes to hold us down."

The marquis cast an anxious glance at the crowd that had assembled to watch them. "I suppose we must not disappoint them," he agreed. "And the mortar has already sounded to tell the people that we are prepared to go aloft."

"There is nothing to be nervous about," de Rozier assured his friend. "I have tried it several times, and with ropes to hold us down there is nothing to fear."

"And if there were no ropes . . . ?" the marquis asked.

De Rozier shrugged. "We would go higher, that is all."

MAN TAKES TO THE SKIES

It was just after noon on November 21, 1783, near the Chateau de la Muette, at Paris, France. As de Rozier had told his friend, he had gone up on several occasions, sometimes as high as three hundred feet before the retaining ropes pulled him down once more. For the marquis, however, there was none of the assurance that accompanied the other's experience. It was the first time that the Marquis d'Arlandes had tried the experiment.

The linen bag was now straining at the ropes which held it down as, a few feet at a time, the men cautiously allowed the montgolfier to rise.

"We are being blown toward the garden wall!" the marquis shouted, but de Rozier had seen the danger and signaled to his assistants to pull them down. One of the ropes had ripped a gash some six feet long in the balloon.

Together they set to work to repair the damage. It was almost two o'clock before they were once more ready, and the crowd was growing restless.

Again the lines were laid out and this time the bag lifted straight into the air.

"We're off!" shouted de Rozier.

The marquis watched the ground falling away from them and felt the excitement of flight flow through his veins. They were over the roof tops now and still going higher. The marquis swept his hat from his head and waved to the cheering spectators below.

"We're almost to three hundred feet," de Rozier shouted to him.

"Cut it loose!" cried the marquis.

De Rozier hesitated for only a second. Then the ropes were gone and the montgolfier was flying free!

It soared skyward carrying the two passengers with it. One thousand, two thousand, three thousand feet! The Seine River was like a narrow ribbon of steel flowing beneath them. Little ants of men walked through the streets of Paris, scarcely discernible between the distant roof tops.

"Look!" de Rozier cried. "The École Militaire and Hotel des Invalides!"

But the marquis did not hear him. He was busy throwing more straw on the fire to carry the montgolfier even farther on its flight. De Rozier laid a hand on his shoulder. He pointed upward.

"Look!"

A spark of fire had touched the edge of the montgolfier. It was burning a hole.

"We must go down!" de Rozier cried.

"We cannot. The houses of the rue de Seve! They are below us!"

The marquis was right. If they were to land now they would descend upon the house tops and perhaps be dashed to the streets below.

De Rozier snatched a sponge from the water container and

hastily beat out the flying sparks which threatened to destroy the montgolfier. He was panting when the final fingers of flame were extinguished.

"We can cross Paris," de Rozier said, his confidence returning. "We can land in the plains beyond."

The city slipped beneath them as the great linen bag settled slowly toward the earth. At last the houses were becoming more and more sparse and were being replaced by the fields and woods lying on the outskirts of the city. Carefully de Rozier applied the sponge to the burning straw until the fire was barely smouldering. As the car lightly touched the ground, the marquis held the montgolfier away from him and leaped out onto the ground. De Rozier followed.

Together they stamped out the remaining embers of the burning straw and commenced to fold the balloon.

They had been aloft for twenty-five minutes and had traveled almost two miles.

Suddenly the Marquis d'Arlandes straightened up with the last folds of the montgolfier in his hands. "Jean," he cried. "It has just occurred to me. We two, you and I, have been the first men to fly!"

De Rozier grinned at his friend. "We may have been the first, my friend," he replied. "But of one thing you may be sure. We shall not be the last of men to sail in the sky."

6: THE CHARLIÈRE

ARE you sure that we have made this balloon just as you wanted it?" Mr. Roberts asked Professor J. A. C. Charles. "We do not understand why you wish to have us coat it with India rubber."

Professor J. A. C. Charles smiled at Mr. Roberts. "The Charlière has been perfectly constructed, m'sieur," he answered. "The coating was necessary because this is not a fire balloon, you see."

"Not a fire balloon?" Mr. Roberts asked.

"No. I intend to fill it with hydrogen which is much lighter than air. It is even lighter than air which has been heated with burning straw."

"But didn't the Montgolfier brothers try using inflammable air?" Mr. Roberts persisted.

THE CHARLIÈRE

"Yes, they did. But the hydrogen was so thin it escaped through the pores of the bag. The India rubber will prevent the inflammable air from escaping."

The Charlière was not as large as the Montgolfier balloon that had carried Jean François de Pilâtre de Rozier and the Marquis d'Arlandes aloft ten days before. In fact, Mr. Roberts feared that it was entirely too small to carry Professor Charles aloft. But if the professor shared those fears he showed no sign. The balloon itself was a splendid sight as it rested in the Tuileries Gardens in Paris, France, on December 1, 1783. Its alternating panels of yellow and red silk fabric glistened in the afternoon sun. An interwoven net hung over the top of the bag and a ring of metal circled it, providing support for the car which hung below. Professor Charles had designed a valve at the top of the bag from which a control rope hung to release the hydrogen and to allow the balloon to descend. The car, hanging beneath the balloon, was equipped with a barometer and with sand ballast. In order to rise, Professor Charles could empty the sand over the sides. To descend, he tugged at the control rope and allowed the light hydrogen gas to escape, bit by bit, from the bag of the balloon.

At last all was ready. Professor Charles presented a small balloon to Montgolfier to compliment him for showing the way. The eyes of six hundred thousand people watched Professor Charles and Mr. Roberts start the slow ascent.

With the controls at his disposal Professor Charles allowed the Charlière to rise to eighteen hundred feet, and unlike those who had flown before him, he could measure his distance from the ground by means of the barometer. In controlled flight a pair of human passengers drifted in the wind.

Where Jean François de Pilâtre de Rozier and his friend the Marquis d'Arlandes had worked frantically to keep their hot air balloon in the skies, Professor Charles and his companion floated gracefully through the air over Paris with little effort. Soon the Tuileries Gardens were lost from their sight.

Little by little the sand ballast was laid over the side by Professor Charles. "It is nearly gone," Mr. Roberts said. "We must descend."

Professor Charles nodded and started the Charlière on its downward course. For almost two hours they had been drifting about through the French skies. Now they were some twenty-seven miles from their point of ascent.

When the last of the ballast was gone the Charlière came to rest in the plain of Nesles just as the last rays of the setting sun were fading from the skies. Scores of country people came to watch it make its landing. The Duc de Chartres, on horseback, came racing to greet the fearless fliers. He clapped them on their backs and excitedly shouted his congratulations to them.

Professor Charles was delighted with the successful flight

of the Charlière and after Mr. Roberts had climbed from the basket safely to the ground, he asked: "I would like to go up once more. Do you mind?"

Mr. Roberts assured him that he did not. Relieved of his weight, the Charlière bounded skyward once more over the plain of Nesles. As the balloon climbed higher in the sky, the professor was amazed to see again the sunset which was no longer visible from the ground.

Reluctantly, as the evening shadows lengthened, the physics professor from Paris brought the Charlière safely to earth for the second time.

Professor Charles and Mr. Roberts had successfully pioneered the use of hydrogen, rather than fire, as the lifting force of lighter-than-air craft. Its use was to become universal until it too was replaced by the safer and less combustible helium.

"This shall be my first and last ascension," Professor Charles told his friend. "My Charlière has proved itself."

From his one and only ascension, Professor J. A. C. Charles led the way for others to fly through the skies. Soon montgolfiers and charlières became common, floating through the air with hot air in the one and hydrogen in the other. Within a few months man was to reach the unprecedented height of 11,732 feet and to travel the unthought-of distance of forty miles, drifting above the clouds that separate the earth from the sky.

Within ten years man was to fly in the Netherlands, Germany, Belgium, and England. George Washington was to watch an ascension in Philadelphia. The English Channel was to be crossed. And Jean François de Pilâtre de Rozier and his friend P. A. Romain were to lose their lives in a similar attempt on June 15, 1785.

Man was not yet flying, but he was learning to float and was learning it well. And with his greater knowledge of the sky, man was beginning to lose his fear of it.

7: ACROSS THE CHANNEL

THE morning of January 7, 1785, dawned
cloudy, just as every morning had done for the past five
weeks or more. But Jean-Pierre François Blanchard, the
aeronaut, gazing from the window of his room in Dover,
England, noticed one small difference. Just above the horizon there was a small patch of blue, a patch big enough to
make a pair of "Dutchman's britches" as the saying goes. A
patch big enough to give hope that the day might clear. Today might prove to be the day when his dream of crossing
the English Channel could become a reality!

Blanchard awakened his friend Dr. John Jeffries, the Boston physician, whose financial backing was to make the flight

possible. Together, the men hastened to the Dover cliffs, there to check the wind and to watch the sky.

By noon their hopes seemed certain to be realized. The sky was clear and the wind blew steadily toward the shores of France. The air was bitter cold, but the men donned heavy jackets and began to make their preparations.

"We can check the equipment, John," Blanchard told the doctor. "We can be sure that we have everything while the balloon is filling."

Carefully they went over the list of supplies. Three bags of sand for ballast, a large parcel of pamphlets, the letter from George Washington to Benjamin Franklin, then in Paris, the cork life jackets, two anchors with cords attached to use when landing, food and water, a compass. One by one the items were counted, inspected, and carefully stowed aboard. The steering oars were attached. At one o'clock the balloon was filled and all was in readiness.

A throng had gathered at the edge of the cliff to see the voyagers off. The carriages and horses crowded about. Some small boats anchored a short distance offshore to watch the balloon ascend.

At last the ropes were cast away and the two men rose smoothly into the air amid the cheers of the people gathered below. Dr. Jeffries waved gaily to them as they seemed to drop away. Blanchard busied himself rowing the air with the oars, vainly trying to steer the balloon toward the water.

What the oars lacked in efficiency the wind took care of, and the fliers watched the coast of Dover grow smaller in the distance. They were on their way to France!

Dr. Jeffries shivered as he looked down at the whitecaps in the Channel. They seemed nearer to him. "Are we dropping down?" he asked Blanchard.

Blanchard peered over the side of the basket and seemed startled. "I should say we are!" he exclaimed. Quickly he reached for the sand ballast. As he poured each of the three bags over the side, the balloon, relieved of the weight, rose higher. But with all three bags gone, the distance between the basket and the waves was none too comfortable.

"How far have we gone?" Jeffries asked uneasily.

"About a third of the way," Blanchard replied. "Or maybe nearer half."

Jeffries looked eastward. Was it land that he could see? Or was it only a low-lying bank of clouds? He was not sure.

The balloon continued to drift toward France. As it drifted, it also continued to settle toward the angry waters of the Channel.

"Let's toss out some of these pamphlets," Dr. Jeffries suggested. "They will be of the least use to us if we are in trouble."

Blanchard agreed. Together they watched first half, then all of the pamphlets flutter downward, to be consumed one by one by the waves.

The balloon drifted on—and down.

"It looks as if we would have to go hungry," Blanchard exclaimed. He threw over the biscuits and apples and boxes of food.

"And thirsty," Dr. Jeffries added, following the aeronaut's example with the bottles of water.

The low-lying cloud in the east was not a cloud at all. It was land! But how far away it looked! And how close the lapping whitecaps that rolled beneath them!

"What about the oars?" Jeffries asked.

Blanchard sighed. His oars were standard parts of his ballooning paraphernalia, but he did have to admit that they had not done very much good in this flight. "Very well," he said. He cut one loose and as it did not seem to have any appreciable effect, he discarded the other. The balloon rose slightly, then again began to sink.

Throwing out the anchors helped for a moment, but not for long. Dr. Jeffries held the compass over the edge of the basket for an instant, hesitated, and then let go. The basket was bare now, except for a few pieces of rope. Blanchard cut these away from the basket and sent them hurtling over the side.

There was a bare hundred feet between them and the waves. The coast of France was nearer now, but still much too far to swim. Dr. Jeffries and Blanchard looked at each other. There was only one hope remaining. They doffed

38

their boots and their heavy jackets and sacrificed them to the hungry Channel. Dr. Jeffries started to send the cork life jackets after them, but Blanchard stopped him.

"No, Doctor. It rather looks as if we might need them. As a last resort, we will cut away the basket and cling to the net around the balloon. We may make it close enough that way to swim to shore."

Dr. Jeffries didn't argue. There was no use telling the aeronaut that he knew something about these things. There was no need to tell him that a man would not last thirty seconds in the freezing January waters of the Channel.

Instead, Dr. Jeffries donned his life jacket and stood shivering in the dangling basket watching the coastline come tantalizingly nearer. It was still four or five miles away.

The water was less than fifty feet below them now. The balloon seemed to hang there, uncertain.

How long they drifted neither of the fliers could tell. The basket was almost touching the waves, and both stood ready with knives to cut it loose, but somehow it never quite touched the water. The land drew closer. A little gust of warmer air lifted the balloon a few feet. Another followed. Then, as the land was almost under them, a surge of warm land air buoyed them up. The balloon rose. The danger was over.

The fliers hugged each other. They forgot they were cold. They danced about in the limited space of the basket.

They had made it!

There was still the problem of landing their craft without injuring themselves and, if possible, without damaging the balloon. Their equipment had all been thrown away long ago. How would they land?

There was a scraping sound under the basket as it grazed a tree top.

"Catch it!" Blanchard shouted, as the idea occurred to them both at the same time.

Jeffries lunged for the branch—and missed. But another was drifting below, and this time the doctor was successful. He held on, watched the branch bend and felt the balloon come to a halt. The branch held.

Limb by limb, the two made their way from the top of the tree to the ground, and to the upturned faces and open mouths of the populace of Calais, France, who had turned out to greet them.

It was three o'clock in the afternoon and they were safely on the ground in the forest of Guines, near Calais. The people opened their arms in friendly welcome, and it was well deserved, for these were the first men to cross the English Channel by air.

Others were to do it later, again by balloon and later still by airplane. But the first time is the most dangerous, the most difficult. Man's flight across the English Channel was no exception to the rule.

8: THE BALLOON COMES TO AMERICA

GEORGE WASHINGTON rose leisurely and dressed slowly. Of late, the affairs of the small and struggling nation had weighed heavily on his shoulders, but this morning he was prepared to perform a lighter duty.

The President sat down to his breakfast and ate without hurrying. He could not forget entirely the pressing problems that had arisen from the Revolution, though that was over and well behind him now. At present, Congress was involved in a long dispute as to whether the states would pay the expenses of the war or whether the federal government would relieve them of their debts. Foreign relations were difficult too. The revolution in France was at its height, and American sympathies had to be watched with care. Only the night

before, Washington had stayed up into the small hours to ex-
amine the latest reports from across the sea. His thoughts of
France reminded him of his engagement for the morning.

Washington finished his meal and strode across the room
to gaze out of the window. The last wisps of mist had drifted
away from the streets of Philadelphia, and the sun was shin-
ing brightly. It was an ideal day for flying. The President
said as much to his attendant.

"Flying?" the man asked curiously. "Yes. I imagine the
birds enjoy this weather." He was a little puzzled at the
President's remark.

Washington smiled. "A wonderful day for men to fly, too."

"Men to fly!"

"Yes. Monsieur Blanchard, you know."

The attendant had not heard of Monsieur Blanchard.
Washington explained to him.

Monsieur Blanchard had come all the way from France
to show this country that he was able to fly. Most of the
people of Philadelphia looked upon his experiment with
doubtful eyes. Man wasn't meant to go up in the air. Anyone who tried was no less than foolhardy. A man who would
try to fly was likely to have other crazy notions. Not that
anyone could actually fly anyway. It was just an insane idea,
a hoax or trick of some kind.

Washington didn't feel that way. Perhaps it was fortunate
that the servant didn't voice his objections or he might have

received an argument. To Washington the prospect of man flying had great possibilities. Besides, Benjamin Franklin, in Paris, had written to him and told him of this wondrous new discovery. Franklin attached great importance to it, and Washington had complete confidence in his diplomat's judgment. Why, who could tell? Maybe some day the balloon would even replace the stagecoach.

It was almost ten o'clock on the morning of January 9, 1793, when the President left the executive mansion on Sixth Street and made his way to the prison court. The balloon was already inflated when he arrived. Preparations were nearly complete.

Washington could see Blanchard bustling about near the bottom of the huge bag, dressed in a plain blue suit and a cocked hat with white feathers. He stood out plainly against the yellow varnished silk of the balloon itself.

There was a huge crowd of people gathered in the prison courtyard. It seemed as if all of the forty or fifty thousand inhabitants of Philadelphia had tried to come together there. Those who could not get in had returned to their homes and were swarming up the sides of the houses to the roof tops. There were sea captains, shipwrights, riggers, lawyers, ministers, bankers, blacksmiths, butchers, and cabinetmakers there, all anxious to see this daring Frenchman climb into the little blue car that hung beneath the balloon, and rise high into the air.

The President saw General Thomas Mifflin, the governor of Pennsylvania, and made his way to his side.

Jean Pierre Blanchard hopped into the basket now, and it balanced only a foot or two off the ground. Mr. Nassy and Mr. Legaux, his assistants, put all their weight on the guide ropes, and with difficulty held the great craft down.

In his hand, the aeronaut held a letter from the President, giving him safe conduct in any part of the United States. The President little realized that he had given the flier the first air-mail letter of the new world.

Blanchard nodded to his assistants. They let go of the ropes. The hushed crowd watched the balloon rise swiftly into the air. They half-expected to see it explode and burst into flames, but nothing happened.

Blanchard unrolled the flag of the United States and then the flag of France and waved them in the air. The crowd sent up a tremendous cheer toward the rising craft.

The wind was from the northwest and it carried the balloon on its course south and east. Several of the crowd dashed out of the prison court and mounted horses, chasing after it. Soon they were out of sight, and the balloon, now high in the air, was no more than a barely visible speck on the horizon.

Slowly and thoughtfully the President turned and retraced his steps to Morris House which he was using as the executive mansion. What future possibilities this travel by air unfolded!

He could see great craft carrying hundreds of men all the way from Massachusetts to Virginia.

Reluctantly Washington dismissed these thoughts and returned to his work. It was not until six-thirty that evening that he was interrupted.

"It is the aeronaut, Monsieur Blanchard," he was told. "He has come to pay his respects."

Washington put his work aside quickly, anxious to know the details of the trip. Mr. Blanchard strode into the office. There were no apparent ill effects from his journey.

"I was in the air almost an hour," he told Washington, "and landed at Deptford, New Jersey."

"Why, that's fifteen miles south of Philadelphia!" Washington was astonished. The stage took much longer.

Blanchard nodded. "At first the farmer who greeted me was afraid, but your letter of safe conduct reassured him. Then several others arrived, and they were good enough to provide me with a carriage for my return."

Fifteen miles in less than an hour! It was amazing to the people of the United States and to President Washington. They knew that there were many difficulties in the path ahead, but they had seen the first American voyage by air.

9: THE FLYING CARPENTER OF PHILADELPHIA

JAMES WILCOX shook his head. "It's going to make a lot of difference when you cut the rope on that contraption," he said.

The members of the Philadelphia Society crowded about him, laughing, and one of them slapped him on the back.

"You wouldn't want people to think you were afraid, would you, Jim?"

Wilcox grinned. "I'm not so sure that I care *what* they think."

"Let the rope out a little more," someone shouted.

Wilcox looked upward. There above him was a cluster of little balloons, forty-seven if he stopped to count. Each balloon was filled with hydrogen, the same light gas that Pro-

46

fessor J. A. C. Charles, the French chemist, had used in Paris.

"Just think, Jim," one of the members of the society, a Mr. Hopkinson, said. "You'll be the first American to fly in a balloon."

"I'm a carpenter, Mr. Hopkinson, not a scientist," Wilcox answered. "And besides, those fellows in Paris went up with one big balloon, not with a bunch of little ones." He looked up again, then hastened to add: "Not that it doesn't look safe enough. It must be all right if you and your friends built it."

"Then you'll try it?"

"Yes," Wilcox said dubiously. "I'll try it."

The balloon was pulled down and made fast to the ground. Wilcox stepped uncertainly into the basket. Closing his eyes tightly, he waved his arm for the man at the ropes to cut him loose.

There was a rush of air as the ropes were cut and the balloon lurched upward. Wilcox opened first one eye and then the other, and looked down at the upturned faces of the men on the ground below. They seemed to be falling farther and farther away from him. The sensation made his spine tingle, but it was far from unpleasant. It made him feel free and independent, and he wanted to laugh. He was not afraid of high places. His work as a carpenter had taken him to many a high scaffolding.

A gentle breeze had come up, and Wilcox watched the

outskirts of Philadelphia slip beneath him. He had been drifting for almost ten minutes when he first noticed the river. The balloon began to settle. Making a swift calculation, Jim saw that he would land right in the middle of it. Even from this height, it looked frighteningly wide. He wouldn't be able to swim to the shore. It was too great a distance.

Frantically, Jim looked for the release valves in the balloons. There were none. The rope, which had held him down before, had been cut close to the basket and it dangled futilely, a bare foot or two long. The river looked deeper and broader as he drew closer to its edge. If there were only some way to make the balloon descend faster!

Jim had an idea. He snatched his pocketknife from his blue denim overalls, and flicked open the blade. Reaching as high as he could, he cut a slit in one of the balloons. There was a hiss of escaping gas as the bag collapsed. Forty-six left. The balloon settled faster.

One by one Jim cut holes in the bags, careful lest he cut too many and dash himself to the ground.

At the very edge of the water, the basket scraped the earth. Jim hopped quickly out, and held the balloon down. The members of the society came rushing up.

Jim felt good inside. He had made the experiment and won. He, James Wilcox, a carpenter, had been the first American to fly!

The flight of James Wilcox, of Philadelphia, is one of the

least documented of the stepping stones in man's conquest of the air. Is it myth or legend or is it fact?

If James Wilcox flew at all, his adventure took place about December 1783, shortly after Professor Charles' first voyage in the Charlière. Most of the earlier writers of aviation refer to it, but the details of the flight are remarkably lacking.

Fact or fancy, James Wilcox survives in the minds of men as a pioneer of aviation. Whether he should be classed with Daedalus and Icarus or with the Montgolfier brothers and Professor Charles, we leave to the reader.

Man was floating fearlessly now through the skies. But he was at the mercy of the winds. It remained for him to control his direction, to fly against the wind, first in lighter-than-air craft, then in gliders, and finally by airplane.

For this next step we must return to France and to Henri Giffard.

10: FLIGHT CONTROLLED

Henri GIFFARD carefully folded back the canvas covering on his steam engine and motioned to his mechanic to join him. Together they checked the bolts which held the engine to its carriage and the ropes which suspended it from the huge cigar-shaped balloon, nearly inflated, which floated overhead.

The Hippodrome at Paris was rapidly filling up. The onlookers, sensing that something new was about to happen, wore quiet looks of expectation. Today Henri Giffard, the French engineer, was going to prove himself a genius.

Or a fool!

For the past seventy years man had been floating through the skies, but always in the direction that the wind had taken him. Henri Giffard was determined to wrest control of the skies from the very wind itself. He had invited all of his friends, and their friends too, to see him win or lose in his attempt.

Henri Giffard was confident. If he failed, as so many others before him had failed, it would not be through any lack of preparation for his flight. As an engineer he had studied carefully the stresses and strains on his airship, the principles of wind resistance, air currents, and speed.

He had studied also the many attempts to conquer the wind, that had ended so disastrously before. Such fantastic theories as having the balloon drawn by a dangling footman or horses, or by a harnessed flock of birds, he had immediately discarded.

But what of the early sails? Or the oars for rowing? They worked with boats. Why not in the ocean of the air above? Because the balloon drifted in pace with the air which offered no resistance to the balloon as water did to a boat, the sails flapped idly in the breeze and were of no avail at all. And although Blanchard had sworn by his wooden oars in 1784, and Roberts by silk-covered paddles a little later, there was no evidence that they had ever done any good even for steering their craft, let alone driving it against the strong force of a heavy wind. Both of these methods Giffard studied, but also discarded.

What was left? There were two possibilities. The paddle

51

wheel was one. Giffard was convinced that it was not quite the solution, but it was as good a starting place as any. From there it was a small jump to the airscrew, or propeller.

The other possibility was the elliptical or cigar-shaped balloon conceived by another Frenchman, General Jean Baptiste Marie Meusnier, in 1784. The shape of the balloon offered less resistance to the wind. Meusnier had tried to direct its course too by hand-operated propellers, but man-power was far too weak to fly against the wind at all.

During the past year Henri Giffard had spent every available moment inventing and building a small steam engine. Tested, it developed three horsepower and weighed only 110

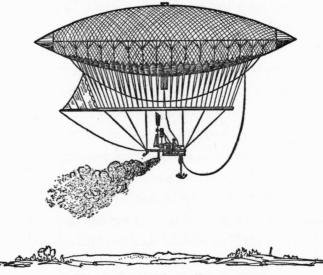

Giffard's Dirigible Balloon – 1852

pounds. With the engine completed, Giffard and two friends had set about making the balloon. Now it was assembled.

The day of September 24, 1852, was an ideal one for the test. The breeze was gentle, yet firm enough to leave no doubt as to its direction.

Compared with modern dirigibles and blimps, Henri Giffard's balloon offered a queer sight to those who had gathered to watch. It looked like a huge 144-foot cigar with pointed ends. It was 39 feet in diameter at the middle, and already over 88,000 cubic feet of coal gas had been pumped into it. Over the whole a network of rope was woven, and a heavy pole hung horizontally at the bottom. To the rear a sail, triangular in shape, acted as a keel or rudder. And under the pole, twenty feet below, was suspended the car, the engine, and the propeller.

The coal gas used to lift the craft was highly inflammable, and it took an extraordinary amount of courage to risk an explosion by placing the furnace of the steam engine beneath it. Giffard's friends had warned him against it, but as a precaution the inventor had covered the stokehole with a fine wire gauze and had pointed the chimney downward.

Henri Giffard swung his feet into the gondola of the waiting airship and wondered if all his preparation would bring him success. He manipulated the controls. The big eleven-foot blade started spinning, at first with a series of disconnected explosions and then with a heavy roar.

Heading the balloon into the light wind that blew across the Hippodrome, Giffard started it on its journey. The nose of the airship went up slightly. It began to move, *against* the wind.

For a long time, Giffard flew the airship over the spectators, now with the breeze and now against it. Then he flew back and forth with the wind blowing from the side. Then he rose to some six thousand feet and flew in a straight line to Elancourt, seventeen miles away. His speed? Not much by today's standards, but then a magnificent 6.71 miles an hour!

This was the birth of the dirigible (steerable) balloon. Man was no longer floating aimlessly about the heavens. He could choose his destination and say: "That is where I want to go, and that is where I am going!"

Henri Giffard had proved that he was not a fool but a genius. He had earned his title which was later bestowed upon him, "the Fulton of aerial navigation."

The struggle now was not between man and nature as much as between two machines both made by man—the lighter-than-air craft of early years and the heavier-than-air plane of today.

The dirigible was to grow to be a giant. Count Zeppelin, the German industralist of later years, made them bigger and bigger, in war and in peace. British and American air liners were to be built. The R-34, the *Shenandoah,* the *Los*

Angeles, the *Akron,* and the *Macon,* the *Graf Zeppelin* and the *Hindenburg* were a few of them, names familiar to all. They carried thousands of passengers across continents and across oceans. But despite their valiant efforts, victory was never theirs.

Instead, there was growing, bit by bit, by strut and by guy wire, another type of flying creature, the airplane. To see how this machine developed we must turn back once more to the world of half-myth and half-truth, to the flight of a French locksmith, Besnier.

First, before we turn so far back in the pages of the history of aviation, let us stop for a moment and consider man's progress. Montgolfier invented the means for man to float, and de Rozier proved that man could do it. Henri Giffard, with his engineering skill, added steering control to man's new skill.

Yet in his struggle to conquer the skies, man had to learn to fall, to fall and not be crushed when he struck the earth. Man had to learn to fall *safely* and be able to rise and fly again. So before we consider man's progress with heavier-than-air craft, let's look at man's other accomplishment, the invention of the parachute.

The Parachute

11: MAN FALLS

ANDRÉ JACQUES GARNERIN pushed aside his notebook and his drawings and stared into space. Like many others of his time he was dreaming of the daring flights that had been made by the aeronauts of France. But unlike the others, he was not thinking of the thrills that went with soaring skyward in the flimsy balloons. Instead, he was thinking of the bursts of flame, the horrified gasps of the crowd, the covered faces, the fall of the airship to the ground.

"It takes a reckless man to fly today," Garnerin told himself. "The people are getting used to seeing balloons go into the skies. To thrill them more the aeronauts build bigger and bigger fires under them to urge them higher. The balloon itself catches fire. Then—poof! At best the flier is badly burned, at the worst he is dashed to pieces on the ground."

He turned back to his sketches. They were all there. The earliest was the umbrella, invented by the Chinese four or five hundred years before. The French monk, Vasson, had translated the original manuscripts from the dusty records in Peking. Garnerin's sketch of the parachute was drawn from the words of the translation. It showed a huge umbrella suspended above the gaping crowds, and under it a dangling acrobat soon to be cut loose to drift downward to the level of his astonished audience.

Leonardo da Vinci's drawing was there too. It was a tent-shaped device which had never gone beyond the model stage, so far as Garnerin could determine. But there seemed to be no reason why it shouldn't work. Da Vinci had suggested that his pyramidal parachute could be used as a fire escape from a burning building or tower.

"If it would make a good fire escape from a burning tower, why would it not be a better fire escape from a burning balloon?" Garnerin had asked himself.

Garnerin was not alone in his belief. A hundred years after da Vinci, the idea had been picked up by Fauste Veranzio, a mathematician who had emigrated from Hungary to Italy. His drawings were more complete, and he even described several successful trials from a Venetian tower. There was no authority for the success of these jumps, in fact none that they were ever made, except the author's own statements. But Garnerin had no reason to disbelieve.

Before he invented the balloon, Joseph Montgolfier had made some tests with the parachute as well. At first he dropped a number of animals from the roof top of his home in Annonay. Then, gaining courage, he tried it himself, and later he jumped from higher buildings before large audiences.

Would the parachute work from the great heights attained by balloons? Garnerin thought that it would.

Most recently another Frenchman, Sebastian Leonomard, had made an even higher jump. He had leaped to safety from the top of Montpelier Observatory, and all France was talking about it.

Garnerin frowned at his notes. The top of Montpelier Observatory was a long way short of his daring idea. Would the parachute crumple? Would it hold the weight of a man for a thousand feet? For two thousand? Garnerin hoped that it would, and for a very good reason. On the next day, October 22, 1797, Garnerin would be that man. Tomorrow, in Paris, with a crowd of invited guests in his audience, André Jacques Garnerin would leap for his life from a balloon.

André Jacques Garnerin was a brave man. He slept well that night.

The parachute was slightly larger than the fourteen-foot

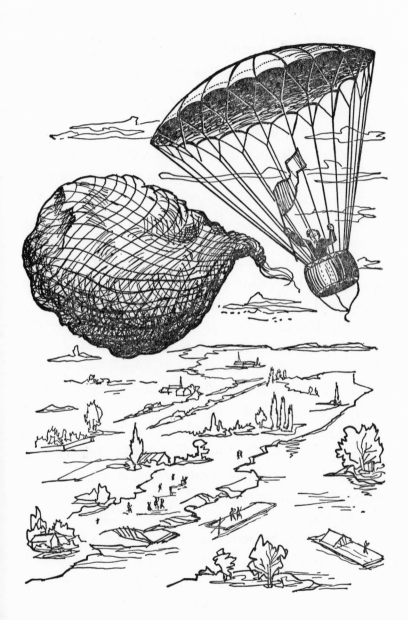

contraption of Leonomard. Garnerin inspected it carefully as the heated air from a roaring fire filled his balloon. Upon it his life would depend.

As the balloon filled, it was allowed to rise a little way into the air. The basket cleared the ground, and under the basket Garnerin's parachute hung. Under the parachute there was another basket, and it was into this that Garnerin clambered. The restraining ropes were cut. The whole contrivance soared into the air.

The crowd watched him expectantly. Up and up the balloon climbed. One thousand, two thousand feet. Then, as Garnerin cut loose, there was a gasp from below. The large balloon and the tiny aeronaut seemed to fly apart. The big linen bag, liberated, shot skyward and burst into flame. But below it, dangling in the small basket attached to his parachute, Garnerin floated downward. He waved bravely at the crowd. A cheer reached him from the throng. Then he clung to the edge of the basket for all he was worth as it began to sway from side to side.

It was still swaying when it landed. The basket hit the ground with a resounding thump. Dazed but unhurt, André Jacques Garnerin stepped safely into the arms of his enthusiastic friends.

The parachute has sometimes been called the life belt of the air. It was born as a fire escape and it was soon to act as one by saving a life from a burning balloon. Garnerin preferred to think of it as a safety measure, rather than as a feat of skill or bravery.

Many of the early attempts in man's fight to fly were dangerous. Most of the pioneers risked their lives in one way or another to provide another step forward in the battle that was yet to be won. Some of them lost. But few brave men have been called upon to take a chance as great as the deliberate one taken by André Jacques Garnerin.

History has not recorded the exact thoughts of this brave pioneer just before he cut his parachute loose from the comparative safety of his balloon two thousand feet from the surface of the earth. History has not recorded his fears or emotions as his frail umbrella swung its violent way earthward. Whatever his thoughts and fears and emotions, those who followed André Jacques Garnerin owe him their undying gratitude for providing them with a fire escape in the air and another great stepping stone, this time down from the sky.

12: THE PERIL OVERCOME

Hot-air balloons were hazardous affairs at best. The bags were made of highly inflammable paper and linen or canvas. Most of them were inflated by burning a combination of straw and wool in a circular pot beneath a vent or hole at the base of the linen sphere. If the burning straw hung too low, it was too far from the opening to feed the hot air into the balloon. If it was too close, the danger of fire was ever present.

As time passed, the crowds of spectators ever willing to watch the other fellow risk his neck expected more and more of the poor aeronaut. To improve his exhibition, to rise to greater heights than ever before, to stay longer in the air than his competitors, the barnstorming balloonist heaped more and more straw on the flaming receptacle, at the same time measuring with anxious eye the distance between the licking flames and the combustible fabric.

If the burning straw ignited the balloon, it was plunged to the ground. Sometimes, if the aeronaut was lucky, the bag would mushroom inside the net, forming a natural parachute and lowering the balloon slowly enough so that only a few broken bones resulted from the overeagerness of the flier. Others were less fortunate.

With the invention of the parachute by André Garnerin, in 1797, early airmen were provided with a means of escape from their flaming craft.

These were the conditions in Warsaw, Poland, in the summer of 1808, when Jordaki Kuparento, a Polish exhibitionist, kneeled down and checked the cord that fastened a huge canvas parachute to the side of his balloon.

"Why do you always carry that thing, Jordaki?" a friend asked. "You never have to use it."

Jordaki rose, brushed off his knees, and flashed his friend a broad smile. "I hope I never do have to use it," he replied. "But it gives me a nice comfortable feeling while I'm up in the air."

"Huh," his friend grunted. "I don't see how you're ever comfortable when that thing leaves the ground. Besides, the only time anyone has ever used a parachute is for an exhibition jump."

Jordaki laughed and clambered into the basket of the balloon. The brilliant July sun beating on the dry ground lifted the balloon rapidly in the updraft. It rose in almost a straight line, for there was no wind. To Jordaki, it looked like just another flight. He leaned against the corner of the basket and looked up at the linen bag above him.

Suddenly his face turned pale. The flames from the fire that was feeding the balloon with hot air were escaping the pot that contained them. Their hungry fingers licked about the thin fabric of the bag. Almost before he had seen it start, the whole balloon was a mass of flames. The basket was plummeting downward.

Instinctively Jordaki clutched the ring that held the cords of his parachute. He closed his eyes and dived head first out of the basket.

It seemed that he would fall through space forever, though actually it was only a split second before his arms were wrenched upward. He was dangling at the end of the open parachute.

At last the ground was close. Jordaki tucked his legs up under him, and as he hit the ground, he rolled with the fall.

Slowly he picked himself up and brushed himself off. His friend came rushing up, an anxious look on his face.

"Are you all right, Jordaki?"

The aeronaut smiled ruefully. "Just a little shaken up, that's all. But I'm afraid I've lost a balloon."

THE PERIL OVERCOME

"You may have lost your balloon, but you've saved your life, Jordaki. The balloon can be replaced, you could not. I was wrong about your parachute. You've proved to the world that they are practical. Yours is the first life to be saved!"

"Perhaps it is the first," Jordaki replied, "but there will be many more. So many that this little incident will soon be forgotten."

"Today will never be forgotten," his friend insisted.

This time Jordaki Kuparento's friend was right.

13: THE PARACHUTE IMPROVED

THE people in the park craned their necks and watched the balloonist above them. Their eyes were anxious.

"Who is that up there?" one of them asked.

"Citizen Garnerin," Monsieur Lelande replied. "He's going to jump in a minute."

No sooner had he spoken than the basket seemed to drop away from the big balloon. It fell quickly at first, then came to an abrupt stop as the huge canvas parachute opened. The balloon, relieved of its weight, shot skyward.

But André Garnerin's troubles were just beginning, for the basket he was in began to swing like the pendulum on a huge clock.

THE PARACHUTE IMPROVED

Some of the men shouted in consternation. Back and forth the basket swung and with every motion it threatened to throw the balloonist out. A woman in the crowd fainted.

Garnerin clutched the basket tighter and watched the ground come close. For a moment it looked as if he would be dashed to pieces on the ground.

The parachute hit the earth and collapsed just as the swaying basket started its upward swing. The fall was broken. Garnerin, dizzy from his ride, stepped out. He was shaken but unhurt.

André Garnerin's luck was still with him. If he had landed while the basket was swinging downward instead of upward, he could have been seriously injured.

The parachute of the early 1800s was far different from the nylon parachute of today. Often it was a canopy made of silk or canvas, held open by a framework of wires or wooden ribs. Usually it hung beneath the balloon. There was no harness, just a basket in which the aeronaut crouched or stood. Later the basket was replaced by a ring or a bar to which the falling flier clung for his life.

The first parachute to rely on air pressure to keep it open was developed by Bourget in France in 1804, but the completely collapsible silk parachute did not appear until 1885 at the hands of Captain Thomas Baldwin. Step by step the parachute was improved. Leslie Irwin invented the folding pack, and S. L. Van Meter, Jr., provided it with a rip cord.

The pilot chute first appeared in Germany during World War I.

Whenever conversation was dull in the coffeehouses of England or the cafés of France, talk turned to André Garnerin's strange new invention, for few inventions have caused more heated debate.

"Anyone who carries this contraption is either a sissy or a fool," some said. "A sissy because they are unnecessary, a fool because they are no good."

John Wise, the now famous American balloonist, set out to prove that he was no sissy. An earlier experience with a flaming balloon had shown him the way.

"If my balloon collapses into its net and lowers me gently to the ground when it is on fire, why will it not do the same when it is undamaged by flames?" he asked himself.

Wise devised a ripping panel by means of which he could deflate his balloon quickly while it was in the air. In 1838, and again in 1839, he successfully exploded his balloon in mid-air, once at thirteen thousand feet, and dropped safely to the ground.

"The balloon itself is a better safety device than the parachute," he told all who would listen.

Perhaps one of the reasons that parachutes were considered so unreliable is that so many different types were tried. Robert Cocking, an Englishman, was a tragic argument for those who believed the parachute to be no good.

THE PARACHUTE IMPROVED

Cocking was a youthful English artist. He had watched Garnerin, now a professional exhibitionist, jump successfully before a huge crowd of spectators, and had been greatly impressed. But he had noticed the one great fault of Garnerin's parachute, a fault over which there was no dispute. The parachute swayed frantically from side to side. At best it made the airman sick, at the worst it could kill him instantly as it dashed him to the ground. Cocking was determined to take the swing out of the parachute.

For the next forty years Cocking worked on models and experimented with new designs. It was not until 1837 that he was ready to make his ill-fated attempt.

Cocking's parachute was entirely different from any tried before. It was like an umbrella, true, but instead of opening earthward, it was like an umbrella upside down with the open side to the sky. The top was fastened to a hoop 107 feet around. It was supported by other hoops and wires. All told, it weighed more than 200 pounds and was made of 124 yards of linen cloth.

Late in the day of July 24, 1837, Cocking made his jump. At five thousand feet he cut loose from the balloon above him. For the first few seconds it descended slowly according to plan. But then the pressure of the air proved too much for the fragile device. The parachute collapsed. The basket broke away from it, and Cocking was plunged to a quick and certain death.

Instead of solving the problem, Robert Cocking had only added more fuel to the public's growing antagonism to the parachute. Small consolation that years later his theory was proved by tests to be sound; his only miscalculation was in the strength of the material he had used! But in the meantime a much more practical development took away the swing, and with it much of the danger, of the parachute.

Strangely enough, it was not an aeronaut at all that solved the problem. It was a French astronomer, Lelande, who had also seen André Garnerin's dangerous drop, and who saw in an instant both the cause and the solution.

"The reason the basket sways is that air is trapped beneath the canopy," Lelande said. "It tips sideways to allow the air to spill out."

The fliers told the astronomer to go back to his stargazing and to leave the business of flying to those who were used to its hazards.

Lelande persisted. "The solution is simple," he insisted. "Just cut a hole in the top of the parachute and the air can easily escape . . ."

His listeners scoffed. It was the air that held the parachute up, they argued. If a hole were cut in the canopy it would allow the air to escape and it would fall too fast.

"The hole must be small—just the right size," Lelande answered his critics.

Man's curiosity was awakened. The idea was tried. It worked. Another bit of progress was made in man's conquest of the sky.

Heavier than Air

14: THE FLEDGLINGS

FROM the first faint glimmerings of history come the records of man's early struggle to fly. Although we are no longer concerned with myth and legend, it must be admitted that the earliest reports are not the most reliable. This is a period of transition, a time when man's dreams mingled with man's trials. Sometimes the proof exists, as is the case with Leonardo da Vinci, who left us his well-filled notebooks. Sometimes the proof is hazy, handed down by word of mouth until it reaches the written pages and becomes believable. Such is the story of an English monk, Oliver of Malmesburg, a student of mathematics and astrology.

Oliver, so the story goes, about A.D. 1050 read of the flight of Daedalus and Icarus. Impressed with the tale, he constructed a pair of wings similar to those described in the legend and sprang from a tower on the edge of the Aegean Sea. He flapped his way against the wind for 125 yards, more or less, before he fell and broke both legs. He later attributed his fall to the lack of a surface on his legs, and because of this he is credited by one writer, humorously at least, to be the inventor of the aerial rudder. There is no record that the monk had any inclination to repeat his experiment.

Man was watching the flying things of the air. If bats and beetles and birds and butterflies sailed through the air on flapping wings, why couldn't man? Little thought was given to the lighter weight of the birds, or to their powerfully developed muscles. Since the early inventors saw only their flapping wings, it was easy enough for them to be led astray. No practical ornithopter, or wing-flapping device has ever yet been demonstrated, and it is unfortunate that so many early attempts were made, based on this theory of flight.

The next trial was that of Giovanni Battiste Dante, an Italian, about 1490. At least Dante could profit by experience. There were to be no broken legs for him! He made his flight over water, at Lake Trasimento, and received a ducking for his trouble.

Not so nebulous are the flights of Besnier, a French locksmith, during the years 1676-1678. His apparatus was peculiar to say the least, but his contemporaries were certainly impressed with the results he obtained. He held two rods, one over each shoulder. In the rear, the rods were attached to his ankles. On each end of each rod was a collapsible plane or wing, rectangular in shape and hinged at the middle, so that they closed as they were moved upward, and opened by the pressure of the air below as they were pulled down.

Besnier jumped from several high places with his contrivance and is said to have soared over buildings with it, but from the description of his wings it seems hardly believable that he could have accomplished everything that is credited to him. In any event, he did not pursue his invention further, but sold the contraption to a traveling showman, and retired to his quiet occupation of repairing broken locks. Strangely enough, Besnier, by his attempt, did little to advance the cause of aviation, but unknowingly he had invented the butterfly valve which opens and closes much as Besnier's wings did, and is so useful in today's machine age.

The next fledgling to try his luck was the Marquis de Bacqueville. He tried to fly in 1742 with flapping wings designed along the same lines as those used by Besnier. His proposed flight was from his home on the rue de St. Pierre to the Tuileries Gardens across the Seine River. He seemed to be doing well, at first, but when he was halfway over the river, he weakened, his wings no longer supported him, and he landed with a resounding thump on a floating barge be-

Besnier's Flying Machine—about 1675

longing to a Parisian washerwoman. He followed the fashion of his predecessors, received a broken leg, and was so thoroughly discouraged that he gave up his efforts to imitate the birds.

There were other fledgings as well. Robert Hooke, an English scientist, tried to invent an ornithopter in the 1600s but gave up in disgust. Earlier Roger Bacon (about 1250) described a similar machine in which the wings were waved back and forth by a turning crank, but he wisely never attempted to fly such a machine.

One of the most unfortunate was Bartholomew de Guzman, a Portuguese friar, who actually obtained the first patent on a flying machine in 1709.

In giving him the sole right to manufacture them, the King of Portugal issued a written decree: "Agreeably to the advice of my Council, I order the pain of death against the transgressor. And in order to encourage the suppliant to apply himself with zeal towards improving the machine which is capable of producing the effects mentioned by him, I also grant him the first Professorship of Mathematics in my University of Coimbra, and first vacancy in my University of Barcelona, with the annual pension of 600,000 reis during his life. Dated the 17th day of April 1709."

Poor Bartholomew de Guzman! Little good was his patent or his pension! The claim was made that his invention was against the laws of nature, and his futile defense that man could fly and still not offend the divine laws was of no avail. He fell a victim of the Inquisition and was thrown into jail. It is believed that he died there, and with him died the secret of his invention.

Such were the fledgings of aviation. They had watched the flying creatures and had been misled by their flapping wings. But misled or not, they had experimented. Nothing can be accomplished without trial. Often nothing can become a success without being first a failure.

Soon, profiting from these earlier failures, was to come a man who also watched birds soar in the wind, but who could realize that a human being could never hold himself in the air by beating it with artificial wings, although he might have a small measure of success gliding in the wind. It was this man, Sir George Cayley, who was firmly to place the next stepping stone in the path to flying.

15: THE RUNAWAY GLIDER

SIR GEORGE CAYLEY and his coach-
man carefully carried the glider to the top of a small knoll.
Behind Sir George puffed a fellow member of the British
Parliament.

Sir George looked over his shoulder toward his tired friend
and smiled at the anxious look on his face.

"You don't have to worry," he reassured the other. "It's
perfectly safe. I've tried it several times. Only this once I
wanted a witness to see it actually fly."

The MP grunted but grinned and wasted no more of his
effort on words until all three men were seated on a boulder
at the top of the hill. Then, after wiping his perspiring brow
with a large handkerchief, he said: "How did you happen

to get started on this flying business anyway, Sir George?"

Sir George shrugged. "I guess it's just a boyhood hobby. I've always had a great fascination for tops and kites."

"Tops? The kites I can understand. But what do tops have to do with it?"

"When I was a lad of eleven," Sir George explained, "two Frenchmen invented a flying top. Their names were Launoy and Bienvenu. They demonstrated their model at the French Academy of Science on April 28, 1784. It made such an impression on me that I wanted to make one myself."

Sir George paused for a moment and watched his glider rock slightly in the gentle wind.

"I did make one later, combining some of the principles of the ancient Chinese tops and some of the ideas of Launoy's and Bienvenu's invention. It was a simple little toy with a cork and four feathers at each end, the feathers inserted in the corks at an angle. A whalebone spring tied at the ends with a strong light cord furnished the power. When the feathers were wound by turning them, the whalebone would tighten in a bow. Then, when it was released, the feathers would spin rapidly enough to carry the whole machine into the air. Whereas Launoy's and Bienvenu's top would rise twenty or twenty-five feet, my top often reached a height of ninety or a hundred feet. So you see, tops as well as kites can be made into flying machines."

The MP was rested now. He had stopped puffing, and the

anxious expression on his face had been replaced by one of curiosity.

"What about kites?" he prompted the inventor.

Sir George was willing to talk about his pet subject. "I suppose kites are almost as old as man himself," he reflected. "Thousands of years ago the Chinese made kites big enough to carry a man into the air. But they were always flown with a cord or string.

"I decided long ago that the inventors who were trying to fly machines that had flapping wings were wasting their time. Why not build a kite large enough to carry a person and then use that person's own weight for a string to hold it against the wind?

"To prove my point I made a model in 1804. It was just a common paper kite fastened to a rod at a slight angle. The rod projected in back to hold a tail and a rudder. This little plaything, even then, skimmed 130 yards all by itself."

Sir George paused and then continued. "I made many more models later, but it was right then and there that I realized I would have to apply a lot of mathematics, yes, and a lot more common sense to designing my kites if I was going to make one that would be stable and carry itself and a man too through the air."

"Like your glider now?" the MP asked.

"Yes. Like this glider. I made model after model and from each one I learned something new. I wrote three articles for

Nicholson's Journal in 1809 and 1810 which I called 'Aerial Navigation' and which contained many of the rules I was able to formulate from flying these models."

"You mean there are rules of flight?" the MP encouraged Sir George. "You can't just build your gliders any way you see fit?"

Sir George laughed. "Far from it! For instance, I learned that for every pound of resistance that I could eliminate, my glider would support thirty pounds of additional weight without any further power."

"Power?"

Sir George nodded sadly. "Power is the one thing we lack. I once even tried gun powder, but it is much too abrupt."

"What about steam?"

"It will do for dirigibles and other lighter-than-air craft, but never for my kites. I studied steam engines for years, but there never will be one light enough to produce the kind of power we need. No, until some sort of an internal combustion machine is invented we will have to glide down-hill with gravity as our only power. Men lack strength to fly by flapping wings.

"But to get back to the rules. I discovered, as I have said, that it was wise to streamline wings to decrease resistance, and at the same time I also learned that curved wings per-formed better. I learned that the center of gravity must agree with the center of pressure on the wings to give balance. I learned that a vertical tail surface or rudder is necessary to keep the glider steady in the air. And if the wings are placed at a slight upward angle from the body, the glider has much more stability."

"And have you incorporated all of these principles in your glider?" the MP asked.

Sir George nodded. "All of them."

Together they looked at the glider. It was a large machine, a biplane with struts and wires between the two wings. In all, its wing surface totaled three hundred square feet.

"It weighs one hundred and forty pounds," Sir George said, in answer to an unspoken question. "Its wing load is about a half pound to the square foot."

Sir George checked the glider for the last time, grasped the lateral supports in his hands and waited for the breeze to blow in just the right direction. He signaled the coachman who had been holding a wing tip steady.

Sir George took a few running steps. An eddy of air caught under the wings. He was airborne!

The biplane glider began to coast at a gentle angle some feet above the sloping ground. The flier's dangling legs were busy keeping the glider balanced.

"Wait! Wait!" the MP called. But Sir George couldn't wait. He was flying now!

The MP and the coachman were scrambling and tumbling down the slope behind him.

Sir George's feet touched the ground again, but the glider was traveling much too fast to land. He leaned back and the nose of the glider lifted for a second. Then he was on the ground again. His legs were flailing to keep up with the craft.

When his coachman and his friend arrived, it was Sir George's turn to pant, and for a moment all three struggled to regain their breath.

When he was able once more to speak, the MP exclaimed: "It was wonderful! Superb! You are the father of British aeronautics!"

But Sir George Cayley has not become known merely as the father of British aeronautics. With the broad base he provided for modern aviation, his child was greater than that. He has become known as the father of aerodynamics throughout all the world. His flying top has become our helicopter, and his angled wings, or dihedral angle, a basic principle of stability in our aircraft of today.

On that day in the early nineteenth century on a gentle hill in England, Sir George Cayley was not thinking quite so far into the future. He was trying to recapture his breath, so he did not answer his friend's exclamations of praise.

He only smiled.

16: IN THE FACE
OF FAILURE

JOHN STRINGFELLOW ran his fingers lightly over his mutton-chop beard and read once more the papers in the folder on his lap. They were in the handwriting of his old friend, William Henson. They were the first optimistic and eager claims Henson had made, long before failure had threatened him or had become a reality to him. They had been written when a huge flying machine was Henson's avid dream. It was to be a machine capable of carrying passengers and freight and mail from Great Britain to India. These papers were a patent application for the first airplane!

The words had been written more than six years before and were addressed to Parliament. The patent was for "Certain Improvements in Locomotive Apparatus and Machinery for Conveying Letters, Goods, and Passengers from Place to Place through the Air, part of which Improvements are applicable to Locomotive and other Machinery to be used on Water and on Land."

How high Henson's hopes had been then! He had been all for rushing headlong into the building of a full-scale airplane.

But John Stringfellow had restrained him. "The motor, my friend, the motor! Where will you find one light enough, yet with enough power?"

In the end both had their way. William Henson, in 1842, had formed the Aerial Steam Transit Company, an organization to raise money for the full-sized project. In the meantime they would build a flying model.

If any light and flat article is thrown edgewise at a little tilt it will rise in the air until it loses speed, the patent specifications continued, and it can be understood that if the article contained its own power it would continue to rise as long as its leading edge was higher than its trailing edge. When the power was stopped or the tilt of the article reversed, gravity would pull it downward if the power was stopped, and gravity would be aided by the force of the power if it were continued, thus imitating the flight of a bird.

Power! The key to success; its lack, the cause of failure.

While Henson was experimenting with his gliding models, John Stringfellow had gone to work on a series of steam engines. Hours of labor went into them, each better than the one before, yet discarded. Each lighter and more powerful, yet still not light or powerful enough.

The members of the Aerial Steam Transit Company were growing restless. The money was coming in more slowly and with greater difficulties. The newspapers of the day stopped publishing pictures of Henson's airplane flying over London or over the Pyramids. The scientific articles which had been so numerous and so evenly divided between arguments for and against Henson's aerial steam carriage were much fewer now, and most of them opposed the inventor's device.

To paraphrase Henson's specifications, the first part of his invention consisted of a machine with a light and strong plane like the extended wings of a bird skimming through the air. Instead of flapping the wings for power, he used paddle wheels or other mechanical propellers worked by steam or a light engine. To control the machine in its flight upward and downward, Henson applied a tail to the plane, which could be raised or lowered. When the power was propelling the machine and the pilot inched the tail upward, the resistance offered by the air would cause the machine to rise on the air; and on the contrary, when the inclination of the tail was reversed, the machine would immediately be propelled downward. To guide the machine laterally, Henson applied a vertical rudder, or second tail, and this was twisted in one direction or the other to control the direction of the machine.

A light enough material! Bamboo, silk, and hollow wooden spars. Wire bracing. An ounce trimmed here, a pound saved there. Strength in the early gliding models was sacrificed to meet the demands of the needed but heavy power. One square foot of surface to every half pound of weight.

The *Ariel* was a name reserved for the real airplane, the one planned to have a wing surface of 4500 square feet with 1500 square feet more surface on the tail. A thirty-horsepower steam engine was to drive its two six-bladed propellers. Looking back, Stringfellow realized how ambitious the full-sized *Ariel* monoplane was.

The model was vastly smaller. Its span was not more than ten feet. But even it was doomed to failure! It was so delicate and fragile, Stringfellow remembered, that the early morning dew had saturated the silk. When the two experimenters went to the field to try their model craft, they found the silk hanging limply from the spars and ribs of the wing and tail, and indeed the whole framework sagged and drooped. They looked at each other in dismay. They might as well try to fly a wet dishrag.

The pair continued with their work for another seven weeks, but it was soon clear that the model was too frail

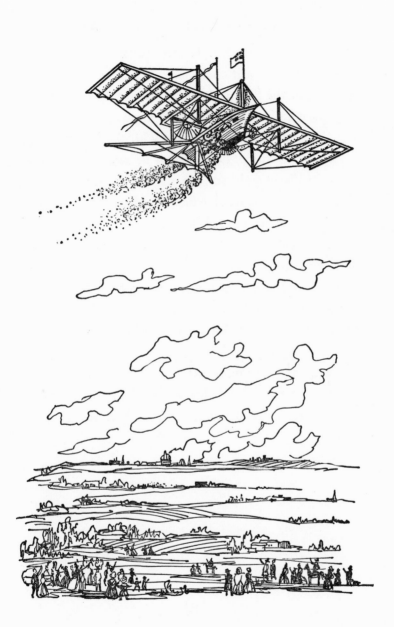

to support itself in the air. To strengthen it properly would add so much weight it could never leave the ground.

Where was the balance between weight and power? John Stringfellow insisted that a lighter engine could be made.

But William Henson, burdened with the failures of both finance and invention, decided that he must try his luck in some other line of endeavor. He married the girl of his choice and took the first ship to America, where he settled down to a quiet life in the state of Texas.

Six years had passed since then. Stringfellow had written to his friend in the New World often, and, he thought, perhaps I should write to him again tonight.

For in spite of all the failures, John Stringfellow knew that his friend was still interested and still believed in his invention.

William Henson might like to know that after six years of labor, John Stringfellow had invited a large group of their fellow scientists, friends, and acquaintances to see him try again.

17: THE FIRST AIRPLANE

JOHN STRINGFELLOW examined his model airplane and wished that his friend in America, William Henson, were back with him again. It would have been a happy experience for him. It would, that is, if the flight turned out to be successful.

The new model was quite different from the original *Ariel,* or the earlier delicate model they had worked on so many long hours six years ago. For one thing, it was smaller and much more compact. Its wingspread was only ten feet and the wings only two feet wide at the greatest point— fourteen square feet in all to hold the tiny craft in the air.

John Stringfellow was not afraid that the model would droop or break from the strain as the earlier one had done, for he had constructed it with care. Even with the tiny steam engine he had developed over the years, it weighed but eight and a half pounds.

But would it fly?

Stringfellow allowed himself no doubts on the success of his experiment. It had to fly. All of the money he had in the world, all that he had earned and saved from his lace factory in Chard for the past almost thirty years had been spent in developing the model that rested at his feet. It was his last chance.

Because it was his last chance, John Stringfellow had invited a number of spectators to witness the trial. He had chosen his guests with care. Especially had he invited the "gentlemen" who had been the first to scoff at his early attempts with William Henson. Among them were the first to heap ridicule and abuse upon the inventors during their early failures. It had been their decision that had sent William Henson to the United States six years ago.

Frederick Marriott was not one of these. He was among the group Stringfellow had invited because of their faith in the two troubled men. Marriott and a few others had believed in Stringfellow until there had been so many failures it had been difficult for Stringfellow to believe in himself.

Ruefully, the inventor remembered when Marriott had called him into his office and told him he was through.

"Why do you try to carry on?" Marriott had asked him.

"Parliament has refused you money to build the *Ariel,* Henson and I have been forced to withdraw from the Transit Company because none of us has the money left to put into it. Man was never meant to fly."

Stringfellow's head had been bowed. All that Marriott had said was true. All, that is, except that man could not fly.

For years John Stringfellow had tried to prove that an airplane could be made to carry passengers. Not merely a glider, a set of wings, but a real airplane with real power to drive it.

John Stringfellow had a deep belief in the dynamic or power theory of flight. Gliding from hilltops was not for him.

"I won't give up," Stringfellow had replied to Marriott. "There is only one way that I can prove my theory. I have a little money saved myself. I'll build a model—a power-driven model, one with a motor smaller than has ever been known before. And if the model will fly, then I can prove that the larger airplane will fly."

Stringfellow remembered this conversation as he stood at the side of the large unused room in his lace factory near Chard, England, that June day in 1848. The airplane was fastened to a special launching device, as it had no wheels of its own. A rod on which it was to run for a few feet was stretched out in front of it. At the sides of the hall the spectators, the faithful and the faithless, waited in silence.

The pressure in the tiny one-cylinder steam engine was high enough now. The two propellers were whirring, and the plane tugged at the cords that held it back.

With a deep breath, Stringfellow bent down and released the airplane. It ran down the inclined wire runway. It gathered speed.

Stringfellow was still holding his breath when it reached the end. Would its eight and a half pounds be too much for the motor? Would it flop to the ground?

It didn't fall. Instead it soared and climbed. The motor turned the propellers faster and faster, and it was beating its way through the air in free powered flight!

It climbed as it approached the far end of the hall. It came to an abrupt halt against the canvas that had been placed there to stop it. Stringfellow paced off the distance. Sixty-six feet.

Marriott was the first to come and shake Stringfellow's hand.

"Congratulations, John," he said. "Your persistence has rewarded you with success at last. No one deserves it more than you."

"Yes," Stringfellow said. "There is one more. William

Henson. Without him, I could have accomplished nothing."

He was sorry that his friend was not there.

John Stringfellow had invented the first airplane to fly. A short time later, near the Cremorne Gardens, he flew the airplane 120 feet; and later still, he was awarded a £100 prize for an improved engine. With the award, with other contributions, and with money of his own, he continued with his experiments.

When Francis Herbert Wenham, a famous engineer in England, improved on the model in 1866 by placing one wing above the other and became known as "The Father of the Biplane," Stringfellow incorporated his idea and went one better, building a ten-foot triplane. It was powered with steam as had been his earlier airplane, and was driven by two propellers, each with six blades. The plane, its engine, boiler, and fuel altogether weighed only twelve pounds. The airplane was demonstrated at the first Aeronautical Exhibition in the world at London, in 1868.

John Stringfellow lived to the venerable age of eighty-four years and much of his long life was spent in the development of his invention.

He fully understood the value of the curved wing and realized the necessity for a proper ratio of power to weight.

By inventing the first airplane to fly under its own power, he had provided a long step forward but his advance was hindered by a great obstacle—a lightweight source of power.

Already Francis Wenham, a founder and charter member of the Royal Aeronautical Society of Great Britain, was studying the natural laws of sustaining heavier-than-air craft in the air, and was building a light gas engine.

With an internal combustion gasoline motor, Stringfellow could easily have been the first man to fly.

But there were still several steps to be taken before man could take to the skies. For the next of these, we must go back to the gliders and the hilltops of France.

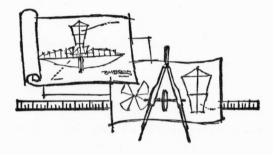

18: THE ANCIENT MARINER

THE great wandering albatross is a huge bird. Its long narrow wings, sometimes almost twelve feet in span, hold its heavy fifteen- or twenty- pound body in the air for days at a time. It glides for hours without flapping its wings, and once it leaves its breeding place in the small oceanic islands of the South Antarctic, it scorns the land for the greater portion of its life.

Sometimes it follows a ship at sea, watching patiently for precious morsels of food to be tossed over the side. More often it settles on the mountainous waves and feeds on cuttle-fish and squid. When it takes flight again it extends its long wings and runs against the wind. If by mischance it lands on the deck of a vessel it cannot take flight and may become seasick with the roll of the waves.

The great wandering albatross has only one rival for size, the condor, which has a heavier body but shorter wings. The albatross is a beautiful bird, white with black wavy bars on its mantle and with black on the tips of its wings and its tail.

When it follows a ship it is an omen of good fortune destined to bring fair sailing winds and favorable weather.

To kill an albatross, as Coleridge's Ancient Mariner did with his crossbow, is to invite the worst possible disaster.

Captain Jean-Marie LeBris killed an albatross.

Captain Jean-Marie LeBris was the third man in history to fly.

Besnier, in 1678, had jumped from a garret and somehow managed to land safely on the ground. Sir George Cayley in the early 1800s had been the next. Now a sea captain, retired from his travels on the water, was determined to conquer the ocean of the air.

Jean-Marie LeBris was tired of the sea. His sun-browned face didn't show his fifty years, nor was it because he felt old that he left the ship of his command and settled down in a quiet little cottage near Douarnenez, France, in 1855.

The truth of the matter was that he wanted to fly.

During his years at sea, Jean had spent many hours on deck watching the beautiful albatross glide gracefully overhead. At first, his interest was inspired only by the beauty of the bird and by its grace in keeping itself endlessly in the air without flapping its wings.

Sometimes he was annoyed that a bird with very little intelligence could soar effortlessly behind the fastest moving ship, keeping pace with it all the way. But mostly his feelings were of admiration for its powerful flight.

"If a bird can do that, a man can too," he told himself over and over again.

On one occasion a bird had landed close in the wake of his vessel, and at other times an albatross had soared by so close he could almost touch it. At every opportunity Jean studied the shape of their wings and their movements in the air.

It was then that in his mind, toughened from hard years

at sea, he knew what he must do. He captured an albatross, killed it, and studied one of its wings.

Remorseful at what he considered a necessary destruction of one of the beautiful birds, LeBris was nevertheless exultant at the result of his experiment.

"I took the wing," he told friends later, "and exposed it to the breeze, and lo, in spite of me it drew forward into the wind; notwithstanding my resistance it tended to rise. Thus I discovered the secret of the bird. I comprehended the whole mystery of flight."

Jean was, of course, slightly wide of the mark. There was a lot to the mystery of flight that he did not comprehend, but he had the will to learn.

Once retired, he set about constructing a glider as nearly like the wing of the albatross as he could remember. If the curse of killing the bird haunted the pensioned sailor, he gave no sign of it.

Fashioned with bamboo and linen, his man-made albatross had a total wingspread of fifty feet. Its body, or fuselage, was thirteen and one half feet long and four feet at its greatest width. By a system of weights, pulleys, and levers Jean could change the angle which the wing made with a horizontal line, called the angle of incidence. In a similar manner the tail moved on hinges both up and down and sideways. LeBris stood inside the framework, working the wing controls with his hands, the tail controls with pedals at his feet.

102

THE ANCIENT MARINER

One Sunday morning in 1855, in Trefeuntec, near his Douarnenez home, he was ready to make the trial.

With tanned arms he lifted his glider from the ground. Its ninety-two pounds rested easily in his strong hands. Ahead of him was the horse and cart, and a long rope stretched between them and his plane. One end was tied with a slip knot to his wrist, the other fastened under the seat of the cart. Assistants steadied the tips of the wings.

Jean gave the signal for the horse to start.

The rope tightened and the horse began to trot. Jean slid along in his glider, slowly at first, then faster. He could feel it grow more buoyant.

The horse, following a turn in the road, brought the glider full into a head wind. It started to rise rapidly, but with stability.

The horse realized something strange was going on and broke into a gallop. Carefully, Jean shifted his weight back and forth, and found that he could control the direction of his glider. He was almost over the cart now. It was time to cast off.

But Jean had underestimated the strength of his glider. Its upward pull had torn the tailboard from the cart. Somehow the driver had been lassoed in the coils of the rope, and he was still sitting on the seat, dangling helplessly in the air.

Jean was nearly three hundred feet high now and had traveled an eighth of a mile, but he had no idea that there was a passenger dangling twenty or thirty feet below him.

He was approaching a rise in the ground when he heard his helper's hoarse shout and looked down in surprise. The fellow was hanging on for dear life and screaming at the top of his lungs.

Quickly, Jean made up his mind. If his friend let go, he would surely be killed. Yet Jean wanted to continue his flight. He was going very slowly now, and by gliding over a rise in the ground he could leave his passenger and continue on.

He leaned back. The albatross nosed up and almost came to a stop. The unhappy helper brushed close to the ground and, landing on his feet, leaped away.

It was at this point that the ghost of the long-dead albatross began to exact its revenge.

Jean leaned forward. It was too late! The dangling driver had balanced him like the tail on a kite. Without the ballast, Jean lost control and the bird-like glider fluttered to the ground, landing on its wing.

Jean picked himself out of the broken spars and torn cloth. He brushed himself off, thankful he wasn't injured. But a rueful look at his albatross disclosed that it was a total loss.

Jean-Marie LeBris had made his mark in aviation history. He had flown. But this had been his finest hour.

Too poor to rebuild the glider immediately, he saved and worked and at long last had a new albatross. He assembled it at the bottom of a quarry and had it hoisted to the top, one hundred feet overhead. Poor Jean! His "complete understanding of the mystery of flight" did not include any knowledge of the treacherous winds in such a place.

Bad luck was still with him, and this time he was lifted out of the wreck, his leg broken.

Jean was out of funds again. His friends tried to help him with public subscriptions, and in 1867 he had completed a new flying ship. He sent it up in too mild a breeze at Brest, but when it rose only thirty or forty feet and flew less than a hundred, his friends deserted him. When he flew it later, fastened like a kite with a strong line, it rose to six hundred feet, and was dashed to the ground and smashed to smithereens.

Discredited as a demented inventor, Jean-Marie LeBris lost his determination to fly. His ill fate seemed to leave him then, but it was only a temporary respite. In spite of his age he served with distinction in the Franco-Prussian War of 1870. When it was over, he retired once more to the quiet occupation of constable in his own home town.

It was there, in 1872, that the ghost of the albatross wreaked its final revenge. Then a special constable, LeBris was set upon and killed by a group of ruffians.

Such was the life of the ancient mariner of aviation, Captain Jean-Marie LeBris, who in spite of his ill fortune contributed so much in man's fight to fly!

19: THE PLAOPHORE

IT IS remarkable, sometimes, how much can be accomplished by a man with an open mind. If he starts his investigations with preconceived notions, his ideas may lead him irretrievably in the wrong direction. But if his curiosity is aroused on a subject of which he knows nothing, he may be directed step by step to the right solution.

Alphonse Pénaud was a young man with an open mind. But Alphonse Pénaud was also angry, and he slammed shut the magazine he had been reading and threw it on the table.

"How do they know?" he said to himself over and over again. "They've never tried it!"

Alphonse Pénaud had just finished reading an article that made fun of man's attempts to fly. It was all too easy, he

106

thought, to say something cannot be done. It was a lot more difficult to prove that it could. Alphonse Pénaud made up his open mind right then that he was going to do something about it.

His friends tried to discourage him. "What chance do you have?" they asked him. "How can you fly when even men who are well and healthy aren't able to?"

It was true. When he was a boy, his health had been so poor that doctors had refused to allow him to enter France's service in the Navy. Not long afterward he had developed a disease in his hip joint which left him forever after on crutches.

Perhaps it was because of this misfortune that Alphonse Pénaud was so successful in his studies of aviation. Since he could not follow the ordinary pursuits of boys and men of his age, he had time on his hands for other things. His leisure time and his intense and open-minded curiosity were to lead to great developments in aviation history.

"There is one thing I can do," Alphonse told his friends who were bent on discouraging him, "I can build a model. If the model flies, then I can build a real airplane and it will fly too."

But which way should he turn? There seemed to be three types of heavier-than-air craft upon which he could experiment. There were the straight-rising tops, called helicopters, there were the wing-flapping machines, called ornithopters,

and there were the soaring fixed-wing types, known as gliders. Power could be added to any of the three to make them
fly.

Alphonse collected all of the books and articles he could
find on the subject of flying. Not that there were many.
Roger Bacon, Leonardo da Vinci and Francis Bacon had
speculated on the theories of flight, but their writings were
only fanciful ideas never put into practice, only the awaken-
ing of a dream. In 1640 John Wilkins, Lord Bishop of Chester, had written a discourse on the art of flying. But Pénaud
was forced to discard most of these early thoughts as unscientific and impractical. He was not concerned with lighter-
than-air ships, nor could he see how chariots could fly or be
towed by birds. No, he must look further.

In a similar fashion he studied reports on the flight of
birds. Borelli, in Rome in 1680, had written *De Motu Ani-
malium* and had decided that man's muscles were too weak
to fly by flapping artificial wings, but at the same time had
developed the idea of varying the angles of wings to control
speed, the basis of our modern wing flaps used today to re-
duce landing speed. Galien, in 1755, had written "The Art
of Navigating in the Air"; Dr. Johnson, in 1759, a "Disserta-
tion on the Art of Flying"; and Paucton, in 1768, an article
on the helicopter. Again Alphonse was forced to separate the
useless from the useful and to reject almost all that he had
read of flights with a balloon.

Nor could Alphonse agree with Thomas Walker, an English artist, who in 1814 proposed that a chariot with flapping wings could fly.

Most interesting of all to Alphonse Pénaud were Sir George Cayley's articles in *Nicholson's Journal* on "Aerial Navigation"; Louis Mouillard's "Observations on the Flight of Birds"; and the results of the model tests made by Henson and Stringfellow.

That was all the research Pénaud could do. There was very little material available in 1870, and most of it was so unscientific that it was of no value at all. However, it became clear to Alphonse Pénaud that of the three theories of flight, the helicopters, the ornithopters, and the fixed-wing craft, there seemed to be very little preference as to which theory he should follow.

"I will try them all," Pénaud told himself, "one by one, and perhaps I shall hit upon the best."

He went to work at once, constructing a helicopter as his first attempt. He mounted two sets of propellers on a stick. One set moved, the other was stationary. He discarded the old whalebone spring power used by Sir George Cayley, and inserted a twisted rubber band along the vertical shaft instead. The helicopter was painstakingly built, carefully balanced, and was a great success immediately. Launched by hand, it would rise fifty feet and fly for as long as twenty-six seconds, a worthy mark for today's toy helicopters to equal.

But Alphonse Pénaud was not satisfied.

"Someday man may fly in such a craft," he told himself, "but it seems an impractical way to start."

In 1871 he began construction of his fixed-wing *Plaophore*. Its wings were shaped like a bird's, its fuselage was a single stick, and its pusher propeller was behind the tail, powered again by a rubber band.

"I must place the center of gravity just behind the leading edge of the wings," Pénaud reasoned accurately, "because the lift is near the front." As a result of this discovery, his *Plaophore,* like all of Pénaud's models, was perfectly balanced.

"I must bend the outer edges of the wings upward," he decided, following earlier leads this time. The dihedral angle gave the *Plaophore* stability from side to side and for stability lengthwise he provided a tail surface at a slight angle from the horizontal of the wing.

After several tests, Alphonse Pénaud offered to demonstrate his model to the Société de Navigation Aérienne, in the Tuileries Gardens.

The members laughed at the idea. "What can a boy of twenty-one prove to us?" they asked. "Especially with a little model that has as its power an elastic band?" But they came to the meeting, if only to laugh at Pénaud.

The *Plaophore* was indeed a small model, the kind boys make today. Its wing was eighteen inches long and four inches wide, its propeller eight inches in diameter. Its weight was 0.56 ounce, of which the rubber band was almost a fourth.

"If this will fly," Alphonse Pénaud told them, "a larger one will. It will prove that man can fly."

The Société members hid their smiles. If man were to fly, it would be in a balloon, not in a contraption like this!

Alphonse wound the rubber band and launched the plane into the air. With propeller turning slowly, it started to climb and to fly in a great circle. Around it went, and around again. When the rubber band was unwound, its nose dropped and it glided gently to the ground.

The Société members were excited, their thoughts of laughter gone. The *Plaophore* had flown! Quickly they measured the distance. In eleven seconds the tiny airplane had flown 131 feet. Together the members of the Société came to Alphonse and congratulated him.

A year later Alphonse Pénaud constructed a wing-flapping ornithopter. Like his earlier attempts the model was perfectly balanced, and hand-launched it would rise and fly for fifty feet. But the model builder quickly decided that this, like his helicopter, was not a practical approach to flight by man. His strongest love was for the fixed-wing *Plaophore*.

In 1876 Alphonse Pénaud and a French mechanic, Paul Gauchot, patented a design for a fixed-wing biplane. Like the earlier model, it had a dihedral angle to its wings. In addition, the wing section was curved and it had a hinged moving section on the edge of the wing, called an aileron. As the air flowed over it, the airplane could be tipped from side to side as it was raised or lowered. Not only was it equipped with a tail surface, but it had a rudder and an elevator, both controlled by one stick—the first joy stick to make its appearance.

Patent in hand, the two inventors searched for funds to build it. But both were inventors, not salesmen. They soon found the public in general and their friends in particular turning away from them. Filled with despair, his money gone, his health failing as well, at the age of thirty Alphonse Pénaud took his own life before it had hardly begun.

What could Alphonse Pénaud have accomplished had he lived his full three score and ten? In the few years between his boyhood and his death he not only provided a fundamental design used in modern aircraft, and a power plant unsurpassed for model airplanes for many years, but he also invented the plane plotting table for navigating balloons, a barometer which anticipated the later altimeter, and a new type of internal combustion engine.

But most of all we should thank Alphonse Pénaud for his demonstration of the *Plaophore*. For with this little half-ounce model he opened many minds which had been closed and proved how foolish it was to say that something could not be done until it had been tried, no matter what the odds were against it.

20: THE SEARCH FOR POWER

HALFWAY around the world, in Australia, man took his next step to conquer the skies. It was a step which resulted from failure, as many had before. It was taken by a man whose greatest flight was sixteen feet in the air and that was neither in a balloon nor in a glider. It was a flight in a man-carrying kite.

Until the 1890s the early experimenters had, for the most part, closely guarded the secrets of their inventions. When Alphonse Pénaud began his researches, you have just read of how few articles and books he was able to find, and most of them had been of little value to him. Lawrence Hargrave proved to inventors that the way to success lay in sharing their secrets with the world.

113

FROM KITE TO KITTY HAWK

Lawrence Hargrave was fascinated by kites. His interest began as a boy when he tried to imitate the fancy designs flown by the Chinese two hundred or more years before the birth of Christ. Soon his hobby developed into a science, and he was building huge kites similar to those used by the Romans, which were said to have carried daring observers into the air to watch the enemy's positions.

Then, as his new interest grew, he studied the kites of George Pocock, the schoolmaster who, in 1826, had lifted several persons from the ground. He studied the construction of other man-carrying kites as well.

From these beginnings, Hargrave soon graduated to "cellular kites" and found that their curved surfaces pulled twice as hard as the more conventional types.

At first he made kites of many cells, but little by little he learned that by cutting the cells down to two, one at each end, he could fly the best kite of all. Thus the box kite was born, and is flown to this day.

The box kite was important for another reason. It provided a design for the airplanes which were to come soon at the end of another decade.

It was a small step for Hargrave to transfer his experiments to airplanes. Unfortunately his greatest interest was in ornithopters, and his earliest models were wing-flapping airplanes powered with rubber bands. Later, he tried the rigid-wing style and the models flew farther with much less power, some of them even traveling almost three hundred feet.

In 1890 Lawrence Hargrave tried compressed air for power. The fuselage of his airplane was a long metal tube in which the compressed air was contained. He succeeded in flying the model for almost four hundred feet.

By now Lawrence Hargrave was considered a freak, and was subjected to the ridicule and laughter of his fellows.

"Imagine a grown man," they scoffed, "flying kites all day, or playing with rubber bands and compressed-air toys."

But he ignored their jibes and published a complete report of all his experiments, while his European contemporaries went on with their work in secrecy.

"What good will it do the world," Hargrave asked, "if all the scientists hide their discoveries, hoping only to make their fortune? The airplane will not be born overnight. It must be built by constant work and improvement. Only by publishing and combining our efforts will we reach our goal faster."

Lawrence Hargrave was quick to realize that rubber bands and compressed-air motors would never create enough power to fly a man-carrying airplane.

To carry a man aloft was now his burning desire.

What could he use for power? Compressed-air motors were light and efficient, but if they were made much larger they would become heavy and unusable.

He would try an "explosion motor." He spent a lot of time

and most of his money trying to build one, using ammonium nitrate, charcoal, and sulphur, the chemicals used at that time as a basis for many fireworks. His chemicals lacked nothing in noise or noxious odors, but they had no power.

The steam engine had not existed very long at this time, but Lawrence Hargrave turned to it next as a solution to his problem. With painstaking care he constructed a steam engine for his eighteenth model—a motor weighing only seven pounds. It produced 0.653 horsepower, (the equivalent of 10.7 pounds for each horsepower) which was by far the lightest ever built. But it was not light enough, and he knew it.

In 1893 he demonstrated this model in the United States. He realized that the power he had created could never be enough to lift a man into the air, but he was never discouraged by his failures. In describing his experiments to the scientists, he said: "The people of Sydney who can speak of my work without a smile are very scarce; it is doubtless the same with American workers. I know that success is dead sure to come, and therefore do not waste time and words in trying to convince unbelievers."

It was only when Lawrence Hargrave returned to his first love, the kite, that he was able to take to the air. On November 12, 1894, in his native New South Wales, near Stanwell Park, three tandem kites picked him sixteen feet off the beach and landed him safely on the sands once more. The inventor described it to the Royal Aeronautical Society the following year as a safe means of experimenting with a flying machine.

The inventor of the box kite was so unselfish in his work, and so near success in his experiments, that he is one of the real pioneers of aviation. Orville Wright was later reputed to have told a newspaperman: "An airplane is a box kite driven by a motor instead of being held into the wind by a string."

If this be so, then no story of aviation would ever be complete without proper credit to Lawrence Hargrave.

21: MAN SOARS

"To conceive of a flying machine is nothing," Otto Lilienthal once said, "to construct one is something, but to make trial of it is everything!"

Otto Lilienthal made trial of his flying machines over two thousand times.

Others before him, LeBris, Cayley, and Mouillard in Europe, and John Joseph Montgomery, the Santa Clara professor, in America, had all taken short downhill hops in heavier-than-air craft, but none had ever controlled their direction. In a simple downhill glide, none had ever reached an altitude *higher* than the take-off point; none had *soared*. This remained for Otto Lilienthal, who by his daring exploits well earned the title "The Father of Gliding."

It began in 1860, when Otto was twelve, in a small Pomeranian village in Germany known as Anklam. Otto and his younger brother, Gustav, had read of the exploits of Besnier, the locksmith, and were determined to have their fling at flying. With bits of linen donated by their mother, and saplings cut from the nearby groves, the boys built wings to attach to their arms and shoulders.

Flapping his way downhill, Otto needed only to crow to look like a scampering rooster. Needless to say, his feet stayed on the ground.

"Perhaps the secret is in the feathers," Gustav suggested.

Together they raided the neighbors' chicken roosts and with tar fastened the feathers to their homemade wings. By now their pals were jeering at them, and tests had to be made in secrecy on moonlight nights. Failure came to them a second time.

Thirty-one years passed before Otto made his third glider. Gustav by now had lost interest in flying himself, although his faith in Otto's ultimate success never faltered. Otto himself had studied engineering, served in the Franco-Prussian War, had become a manufacturer, and had amassed a comfortable fortune. During all this time he had studied bird flight, particularly the flights made by the stork, a common bird in Pomerania.

"The third time, I shall not fail," Otto told himself. He was right, and although he may not then have realized it, there were three very good reasons for his success.

The first of these was his engineering skill, which taught him that a curved or cambered wing would lift more readily, and that a glider need not be large to lift a man. His knowledge enabled him to build his craft light in weight but sturdy in construction.

Second, his exhaustive study of birds had shown him many of the secrets of their flight. Probably most important, he had noticed that storks always took off *into* the wind. Earlier experimenters had sought to take off with the wind behind them thinking they would be pushed along by the breeze at their back. Also, Otto noticed the short wavering flights of the baby storks, and determined then and there that he must start on a small scale and work up to larger things.

"My brother Otto used to say that 'man must serve an apprenticeship to the birds,'" Gustav once said. Otto had decided to do just that. Two years before his first glider flight he published the results of his long studies in a treatise called "Bird Flight as the Basis of the Flying Art."

Third, Otto's own acrobatic agility and the skill that he had developed from his small beginnings assured him of a successful venture with his new man-made bird.

Otto's first craft was a monoplane whose wings, bird-shaped, were constructed of peeled willow wood and waxed cotton fabric. Their area was a scant 160 feet. In the center curved wooden supports left an opening for the pilot's body to hang through. Altogether it weighed fifty pounds. Like

120

the baby storks, Otto started to fly in a small way. In his garden he would run a carefully measured twenty-six feet and jump from a springboard. He was delighted to make short flights of ten or fifteen yards and to learn to balance his ship by twisting his legs and his body to its highest side.

Soon he was ready for longer flights.

He cut a circular hangar into the crest of a slope near Steglitz and in it stored his glider, now greatly improved. For three months he waited in vain for a proper wind. To his dismay, he had selected a slope which ran with, rather than against, the prevailing winds. He moved to the low Rhinow Hills, and there made many glides over the green meadows.

It was in 1894 that Otto's real chance came. A canal was being constructed near Berlin, close to Otto's home. He quickly arranged to have the dirt piled in the middle of a field, and thereafter from the height of his artifical hill he was able to fly in whatever direction the wind willed for him. Near the top of the fifty-foot mound he built a cave-like hangar where his glider, now with folding wings, was stored.

Otto retired from his business and devoted his entire time to "air sailing," as he called it. Where he had flown before on nearly every Sunday, he now spent most of his weekdays on his man-made hill. He constructed other gliders, one of them a biplane. The latter he found much more difficult to control by shifting his weight, but it had a great deal more lift, and often he found himself considerably higher in the air than the place where he had taken off. He had become the first man to soar.

Otto became completely at home in the air. He began to make slight turns, then sharper ones, sometimes as much as 180 degrees. People traveled from Berlin to watch this peculiar fellow pursue his odd sport of "air-sailing." Then they came from the rest of Germany, from Europe, and from all over the world. Always their first amusement changed rapidly to admiration.

Otto took full notes on every flight he made and published them freely for the use of all who were interested. "To those who from a modest beginning and with gradually increased extent and elevation of flight have gained full control of the apparatus it is not in the least dangerous to cross deep and broad ravines," he wrote. "It is a difficult task to convey to one who has never enjoyed aerial flight a clear perception of the exhilarating pleasure of this elastic motion. The elevation above the ground loses its terrors because we have learned by experience what sure dependence may be placed upon the buoyancy of the air."

Lilienthal loved to fly over the heads of the throng that was watching him and to hover momentarily in the air and shout directions to the many photographers below.

Then one day, in 1896, the sport proved that it *was* dangerous, and that in spite of his great skill, the buoyancy of

the air was not as dependable as Otto had believed it to be. Caught by a fickle gust of wind while he was testing a new type of control designed for use by less agile men than himself, the father of gliding lost control of his craft. He was plunged to the earth and died a few hours later.

In Lilienthal's five years of flying, the Wright brothers estimated that Otto spent only five hours, in all, in the air. He made over two thousand flights, some as long as a thousand feet.

Between 1891 and 1896 he had become complete master of his several ships, and his analysis of each flight proved an invaluable aid to the many disciples he left to carry on his work—Percy Pilcher, Octave Chanute, and the Wright brothers themselves. The airplane was near at hand. Nearer than before, because Otto Lilienthal gave so freely of his efforts and of his skill.

He also gave his life.

22: THE BAT,
THE BEETLE, THE GULL,
AND THE HAWK

MAN'S contest with the birds was now in full swing. Leonardo da Vinci had watched all kinds of flying creatures, while Jean-Marie LeBris had concentrated on the albatross. Louis Mouillard was interested in the larger birds, particularly the vultures of Africa; Thomas Walker justified his flying chariot by comparing it to the condor. John Montgomery, the American, used to shoo his sister's hens to watch them flutter into the air. And Otto Lilienthal had studied the bats and storks that flew over his home in Germany.

Percy Sinclair Pilcher, an English marine engineer, in 1895 decided that the bat was the creature for him.

125

The first man-made bat which he constructed was of bamboo and cloth. It was small and light, weighing only forty-five pounds. But before he took to the air, Percy Pilcher decided that he should talk to someone who had developed a little more experience in the art of air sailing. Thus it was that in 1895 he journeyed to Berlin to have a chat with Otto Lilienthal.

The master of gliding was more than happy to talk with anyone interested in this new science, and the pair became close friends. Pilcher even tried the Lilienthal biplane glider on a few gentle slopes. He returned to England an enthusiastic follower of the German aviator.

The *Bat* was remodeled, its excessive dihedral angle cut down from four feet to six inches at the wing tips and a horizontal tail added. The *Bat* began to fly!

But Pilcher was not satisfied.

His second craft was called the *Beetle*. It was larger than the *Bat* and it had long squared wings with clipped corners. It weighed eighty pounds and its wings had an area of only 170 square feet. It was sluggish in the air and never flew far.

Percy Pilcher soon abandoned the *Beetle* and built the *Gull*. Its greater wingspread but lighter weight of only fifty-five pounds made it too frail to use in any kind of breeze, and it was replaced almost at once by Pilcher's last glider, the *Hawk*, very much like his first one. In the summer of 1896, the *Hawk* was ready to fly.

"This one is best of all," Percy Pilcher said, looking proudly at his new craft. "It's better than all the others." The glider was resting on top of a small hill. Pilcher's assistant was fastening a tow line to it and to a pair of horses nearby.

Pilcher's friend looked anxiously across the valley. "Do you think you can make it?" he asked. He didn't like the long rough spot at the foot of the hill.

Pilcher was calm. "I'm sure I can," he answered. "The horses will stop just before they reach those stones down there. By that time I'll be high above them."

"Suppose something goes wrong? Remember LeBris when he picked up the driver of his cart and scared the poor fellow half to death?"

Pilcher laughed. "I remember. It was lucky the fellow was only scared. But we have no cart here, and I've improved the method of casting off the tow line. Besides, the *Hawk* is very stable. We've taken all the flaws out of it—it's the fourth glider we've built, you know, after Lilienthal helped us."

"I know," his friend admitted. "But I just can't help worrying."

Pilcher laughed again, and with a nod to his assistant, climbed into the opening between the wings. As in his other ships, his forearms rested along the framework, and his legs hung below. He looked fondly at the wings that stretched outward on either side, wings of bamboo covered with cloth.

He nodded toward the horses without glancing at the patch of rocks at the foot of the hill below him.

The horses, released at last, galloped down the hill. Pilcher took a few running steps, for his glider had no wheels. In a few feet the weight shifted from his legs to his arms, and he found himself floating through the air.

The horses reached the foot of the hill and stopped. The glider rose above them. Pilcher was flying over the stones now. With a quick motion he cast off the tow line and was free.

Swinging his legs back and forth, and sideways, he kept the little craft precariously level. He had little time to think, his maneuvering kept him so busy.

The other side of the valley was approaching now, and with it a rise too high to climb over. Reluctantly Pilcher leaned his body forward, and the *Hawk* nosed down.

He touched the ground lightly and ran again for a few steps until the weight of the airplane settled in his arms. The flight was over!

Together Pilcher, his assistant, and their friend measured the distance. Eight hundred feet! It was the longest flight Pilcher had ever made.

Dreamily, Pilcher looked into the blue sky dotted with small clouds that scudded with the wind. "Some day," he said, "we will find a motor that will be light enough. Some day we will carry our horses with us, and when that day comes, we'll be able to fly perhaps a whole hour at a time."

Altogether Percy Pilcher made eleven other successful glides in the *Hawk* during the summer of 1896.

Then he started construction of a triplane glider, a much larger affair to which he was to add a motor, if early trials proved that it could glide successfully without power. A demonstration was scheduled for September 30, 1899, at Stamford Hall, Market Harborough.

It was a misty wet day, but Pilcher could not disappoint the crowds that had gathered. For safety's sake, he decided to use the *Hawk* instead. On his first attempt the tow line parted, but the *Hawk* had handled well, and he decided to try again. Well soaked by this time, the *Hawk* took off heavily. Its tail snapped, and the disciple of Lilienthal, like his predecessor, was plunged to his death.

Percy Pilcher died at the age of thirty-four. Had he lived another forty years he could have seen some of the miracles aviation was to bring.

In his short years of flying Percy Pilcher had proved again that man could fly, that he himself was close to flying even then. He brought back the shock-cord launching method tried by LeBris, using a long stretchy rope to sling-shot his craft into the air. In his later but never-tested machine, he had developed a type of landing gear.

With the help of Percy Pilcher aviation had taken another step in its march toward success.

23: AN ENGINEER
TAKES TO THE AIR

O TTO LILIENTHAL, the German
master of air sailing, had not only been the father of gliding
but also the parent of a whole school of thought. Dozens of
disciples started experiments in different parts of the world.
Most were imitators, but two, at least, carried on with Lilienthal's work where he had been forced to leave it.

The first of these had been Percy Pilcher, the English
marine engineer. The second was an engineer too, but there
the resemblance ended.

Percy Pilcher died at the age of thirty-four. Lilienthal's
other disciple did not begin to experiment with gliders until
he was sixty-four.

Percy Pilcher died in the crash of one of his gliders. The

other disciple and his assistants made thousands of flights without a single accident.

Percy Pilcher constructed his planes after the fashion of birds, doing his best to imitate them. The second engineer moved step by step through mathematical precision and did not attempt construction until he was assured of absolute success.

A Frenchman by birth, a United States citizen by naturalization, the second disciple during his earlier years was a brilliant engineer whose bridges and railway structures still exist in the Middle West.

His name was Octave Chanute.

Octave Chanute first displayed his interest in aviation when he published, in 1891, a group of articles entitled "Progress in Flying Machines."

Five years elapsed before Octave Chanute built and flew his first glider, and then it was modeled closely on the craft that were being flown by Lilienthal in Germany.

Chanute made several of the early flights himself and was quick to realize two difficulties. First, that controlling the gliders by shifting weight was a hazardous and makeshift arrangement at best; and second, that at his age such agility was beyond the bounds of reason. He was able to make only short glides. He employed two able assistants, Augustus Herring and William Avery. Herring was himself an engineer and had worked with Lilienthal in Germany. Later

flights, except when some new control or device was being tested, became the special province of the assistants.

Chanute turned his attention to the problem that attracted him most, the problem of automatic stability. In 1897 five gliders had emerged from his shop, and four to six men were in his employ turning out newer models.

Wings were his first object of research. His five-winged quinque-plane resembled somewhat the glider of Horatio F. Phillips which had so many slat-like wings it was nick-named "the venetian blind," or one of Alexander Graham Bell's later many-winged attempts. It made about three hundred glides. But Chanute discovered that the extra wings were unnecessary, and settled upon the biplane for his later models.

Strength was his next study, and it was not long at all

before he had developed a system of struts and bracing to be used in later powered biplane flight. His experience in building bridges stood him in good stead during this period of his research.

Next Chanute turned to the matter of control. Adjustable wings were added, and an undercarriage and control levers. Although the flier still had to shift his weight to a considerable extent, he did not have to be an acrobat to keep himself in the air.

A camp was set up on the sand dunes near Lake Michigan, and a launching platform similar to a small ski jump constructed. Five new gliders were built, tested, and made over eight hundred glides there.

Lilienthal had been hesitant to take off in winds of more than thirteen miles an hour. With his improvements Chanute launched his gliders in the stiff winds coming over Lake Michigan with a velocity of over thirty miles an hour. Lilienthal and Pilcher had flown at slow speeds, a few miles an hour, but Chanute's gliders performed at an average speed of between twenty-two and thirty miles an hour, and on one occasion reached the high of fifty-two miles an hour.

So certain and safe had the engineer built his ships that every now and then an interested spectator was allowed to fly one, when conditions were mild and there was time for one of the assistants to give them proper guidance.

Unlike Lilienthal, Pilcher, or any of his contemporaries,

Octave Chanute was not hampered by the ambition to add power to his gliders. He felt that this would come eventually, but that the problems of stability and control must first be conquered.

Man would eventually fly. He believed that strongly, but he also believed that this would come about "by a process of evolution: one experimenter finding his way a certain distance into the labyrinth, the next penetrating further, and so on . . . until success is won."

It was the turn of the century now, and Octave Chanute, in addition to his experiments, was taking frequent trips to Dayton, Ohio, and to a remote place called Kill Devil Hill, near Kitty Hawk, North Carolina.

He had made the acquaintance, he told his assistants, of a couple of bicycle manufacturers from Dayton. They were interested in flying too, and he wanted to pass on to them as much information from his copious notes as he could.

Their names? They called themselves the Wright brothers.

24: STEPS ASIDE

As THE world entered the twentieth century the heyday of gliders was coming to a close. They were soon to be replaced by powered flight. It is true that they have continued to the present day, but only as a sport. Their contributions to the first powered airplane had been completed.

In the story of any great invention, however, there are many pathways. There is the main or central one which we have been following with the story of aviation. But there are many others as well. Sometimes the pathways cross each other, and do not meet again. Such would be the pathway of the steam engine, which was used to power early planes but was later discarded.

135

Sometimes the pathways merge and continue along to-gether. For instance, Hero propounded the principles of jet propulsion about 150 B.C., starting a long pathway of progress into the future. This pathway merged with that of the air-plane, but much later and after flight was well established. Already the pathway of kites, starting with their invention by the Chinese about 200 B.C., had merged with aviation and was following its course.

Another example of such a merger was taking place in 1900. It was the pathway ending with the invention of the gasoline motor.

Several of the early pioneers had searched for a light and powerful engine to drive their machines through the air. A few had foreseen the internal combustion engine. It remained for Gottlieb Daimler to complete the work and to construct a motor fueled with gasoline which fulfilled both require-ments.

In 1897 David Schwarz, a Hungarian living in Germany, was quick to adapt the motor to his new aluminum rigid dirigible. It was the first airship to use a gasoline motor. So effective was it that Count Ferdinand von Zeppelin accepted it (and improved it) almost immediately for use on his much larger ships.

Two more attempts were to be made to harness steam as a motive power before it was at long last abandoned. Then the Wright brothers built their own gasoline engine of

Dirigible Balloon of Count Zeppelin – 1900

aluminum, and history has recorded the result of their choice.

There were other contributions which came from off the beaten path. One of these was the invention of the wind tunnel in 1877. When things went wrong with the Wright brothers' experiments they constructed their own wind tunnel and soon found the source of their difficulties. Today, the wind tunnel, a hollow tube in which plane models are suspended and subjected to high winds created by huge fans, is an invaluable tool for testing new devices.

The development of the airplane propeller followed a sequence of interesting experiments. It was conceived and used by Leonardo da Vinci about the time Christopher Columbus discovered America. General Jean Baptiste Marie Meusnier, in 1784, made the first workable propeller and tested it on his cigar-shaped balloon. Hand-cranked, it attained speeds of about three miles an hour. Monck Mason, an early balloonist, after a flight in the Great Nassau balloon, in 1843 devised a workable aerial screw. It was in a full circle rather than an arc, and looked like the end of a meat grinder. It was driven, by means of a clockwork, at a sufficiently high speed to drive a model dirigible at a speed of six miles an hour. Hugh Bell, an English physician, placed a hand-cranked propeller on his balloon in 1850, but at each trial the wind was so strong that it was doubtful if the propeller helped him. It remained for Henri Giffard, in Paris, to prove that a steam-driven propeller could be used to navigate a dirigible over a plotted course. At last man was able to break away from the deep-seated theory that because a bird flapped its wings to fly, man must do the same. From this point on, the pathways of propeller and plane merged, and the aerial propeller performed the labor of pulling man-made birds through the skies.

Man was almost ready to fly, but on the eve of his success a greater battle was raging between the proponents of lighter-than-air craft and the advocates of heavier-than-air flying machines. With Henri Giffard's controlled flight in 1852, followed by the invention of the rigid airship by Joseph

Speiss in 1873, man already had a fairly efficient, but expensive, method of carrying not only himself, but numerous passengers through the air. The wealthy Brazilian, Alberto Santos-Dumont, was dazzling all Paris with his daring exploits in his lighter-than-air craft, and had even persuaded the lovely Aida de Costa to pilot his *Runabout* by herself. Bicycling desperately below, Santos-Dumont arrived just too late to prevent the first woman pilot from landing in the middle of a polo match at Bagatelle.

Was not flying these huge machines adventurous and glamorous enough for anyone? Shouldn't man be satisfied?

But man was not satisfied—at least a few men were not content to fly through the air like elephants. They still had the driving urge to fly like birds.

Now so close to success, they meant to claim it as their own.

They carried on with their work.

25: THE FLYING GIANT

SIR HIRAM MAXIM is best known for the invention of the machine gun that was named after him, but far more fascinating is the tale of his single attempt to invent the airplane. For in this attempt he built the largest airplane constructed up to that time; he spent over a hundred thousand dollars doing it, and yet he took every precaution possible to prevent it from flying.

Most surprising of all, in spite of all his precautions to hold it down, Sir Hiram Maxim's air monster left the ground.

Sir Hiram Maxim was a man of forceful moods. His friends said that he had positive ideas, his enemies said he was just plain cantankerous.

THE FLYING GIANT

Born in Maine, he had moved to Great Britain after disagreement with the United States government over the patents for his machine gun.

It was while living near Bexley, in Kent, England, that he developed a keen dislike for lighter-than-air craft.

"It is quite as impossible to propel a balloon with any velocity through the air as it is for a jellyfish to make high speed," he said.

In 1893 he began to put his dislike of lighter-than-air flying into action. By whirling models at the end of an elaborate arm two hundred feet in length and at speeds sometimes as high as ninety miles an hour, he studied wing lift, balance, and the thrust of propellers.

After exhaustive experiments with his heavier-than-air models, Sir Hiram Maxim was ready to try out the real thing. Realizing that steam power would be heavy, he built a huge air monster, hoping by its size to compensate for the weight of its two motors. Before it was ready for the test, a ten-mile breeze toppled it over, as if to prove the power of the wind against the man-made juggernaut.

Three-thousand-pound wheels, meant to hold it down, were discarded. A half mile of nine-gauge railroad track was laid upon which the airplane was to run, and guard rails of squared pine logs were installed alongside. Outriggers under the guard rails would hold the monster down so that it could rise no more than two feet.

On July 31, 1894, the airplane was ready for its trial run.
Pressure was building up in the huge 363-horsepower engines when Sir Hiram arrived and took charge of the situa-
tion. The huge airplane, its main wing 110 feet long and its
body stretching 145 feet from tip to tip, rested on the rails.
Altogether it weighed two and a half tons. It had weighed
four tons before the heavy wheels had been eliminated.

"You have an ideal day for your test, Sir Hiram," an assistant said. "Are you going to use its full power?"

"Full steam today, young man," Maxim replied.

He climbed into the seat and tried the controls. He made sure that his instruments were in order while he waited for his assistants to tell him that all was in readiness. There was a speed indicator and an instrument to tell him how much lift the wings were providing. At last the signal came.

The propellers, over seventeen feet in diameter, began to turn faster as he eased the throttle ahead. Gas from 6000 jets (he had reduced the number from 45,000) burned to produce steam. The vapors began to condense inside the hollow steel tubes that provided the framework for the craft. The pressure indicator showed the steam pressure at two hundred pounds.

There was a hiss of steam and the giant jerked forward with almost enough force to knock over the assistants standing nearby. It began a lumbering, bouncing trip down the half mile of track ahead. Sir Hiram advanced the throttle.

The steam pressure went up and up as the plane's speed increased. The propellers whined, turning up four hundred revolutions a minute. At 320 pounds, there was a sudden "pop" as the safety valve blew, and a cloud of steam followed the airplane, making it look for all the world like a ship from Mars.

Sir Hiram gritted his teeth and continued to press the throttle forward. He had used up six hundred feet of his track now, and all four outriggers were pressing against the undersides of the guard rails. The monster was "flying" two feet off the ground, with only the guards against it and the blue sky above!

The outriggers tugged harder and harder as the machine thundered along the track.

Sir Hiram, at nine hundred feet, could feel the jolt as the wheel at his left broke through the guard behind him and came loose. The rear of the machine soared skyward. A moment later the front left wheel broke loose too, and then the right.

The machine was free! It was rising!

The throttle had notches to go. There were still fifteen hundred feet of track ahead, although that was useless now. Sir Hiram was in the air. He was flying! But what should he do? If he pushed the throttle ahead, his airplane would gather speed, it would rise, and he would be the first man to fly a powered airplane. But he had no landing gear. If he tried to fly he would most certainly be killed.

Reluctantly, Sir Hiram pulled the throttle back, and the big plane, the hundred-thousand-dollar plane, settled to the ground. Its underside struck the soft turf and it keeled over on its side. Gingerly Sir Hiram stepped unhurt from the complete wreckage of his plane.

In his account of the trial Sir Hiram wrote: "The first part of the track was up a slight incline, but the machine was lifted clear of the lower rails and all of the top wheels were fully engaged on the upper track when about six hundred feet had been covered. The speed rapidly increased, and when nine hundred feet had been covered, one of the rear axletrees, which were of two-inch steel tubing, doubled up and set the rear end of the machine completely free. . . . The rear end of the machine, being set free, raised considerably above the track and swayed. At about one thousand feet the left forward wheel also got clear of the upper track, and shortly afterwards the right forward wheel tore up about one hundred feet of the upper track. Steam was at once shut off, and the machine sank directly to the earth, embedding the wheels in a soft turf without leaving any other marks; showing most conclusively that the machine was completely suspended in the air before it settled to the earth. . . . The total lifting effect upon the machine must have been at least ten thousand lbs."

Once was enough for Sir Hiram Maxim. He never tried to build another airplane, nor did he ever attempt to fly again. But in his one test he had proved that an airplane could be made to lift itself and its motor from the ground, that, unlike lighter-than-air craft, it could fly at a high speed, and that a screw propeller rather than a flapping device was the proper way to translate power into motion.

In his own words: "Propulsion and lifting are solved problems; the rest is a mere matter of time. Give us the light motor and we will fly."

145

26: DID IT FLY?

IN France there are many who believe that the distinction of being the first to fly does not belong to the Wright brothers, but that the honor belongs to a modest French electrical engineer. The French themselves are divided on the subject, as are those who witnessed the trial of the *Avion,* on October 14, 1897, near Satory, France.

Years before, in 1872, Clement Ader, the young engineer, had borrowed eagles and bats from the Zoological Gardens and had studied their habits in the air. He had tried his skill on a full-sized ornithopter then, and like so many before him had discovered that man's muscles lacked the necessary power to lift him from the ground by flapping his wings.

Ader lost interest for a time then, and went on to invent

some telephonic and electrical devices that amassed a comfortable fortune for him. Fourteen years elapsed before he returned to aviation.

He read *Studies of Large Birds,* which Louis Pierre Mouillard had written some years before. Mouillard had studied vultures while living in Egypt and his book dealt fully with them. Clement Ader was impressed by these studies, and decided he must study the birds in person. He traveled to another part of Africa, a place near Constantine, Algeria. He found no vultures there. Undismayed, he hired two guides, disguised himself as an Arab and journeyed into Arabia. There he decoyed the vultures with chunks of rotted meat and found ample details for his notebook.

His first airplane, the *Éole,* resembled a bat more than it did a vulture. But it had fixed wings. His studies had revealed to Ader that the larger birds soared with their wings outstretched more than by flapping them.

Clement Ader tested the *Éole* in secrecy. It was a large machine, its wingspan fifty-four feet. It was driven by a steam engine and propeller. Racing across the fields at the Chateau d'Amainvilliers, it attained a speed of thirty-six miles an hour. Ader claimed that the *Éole* flew, and two witnesses supported him, but the claim has never been accepted in history.

The ground speed of the craft did, however, attract the attention of De Freycinet, the French Minister of War, and after Ader had built another craft, called the *Avion,* and had spent most of his money, a sum upwards of a hundred thousand dollars, the French government granted him funds to build a third ship.

The *Avion II* is the airplane upon which Clement Ader must rest his claim to fame.

The scene was set, the aircraft ready.

Clement Ader watched the sun going down over the western hills of France and his patience went down with it. The weather was clear, but all afternoon the wind had been gusty. Too gusty for him to launch the *Avion.* What could he do? It was five o'clock now, and the little group of spectators had been waiting hours for the flight to take place.

General Mensier had seen the *Avion* take several hops two days before, on October 12, 1897. He had brought two of his friends in the French Army and two engineering professors to the military reservation at Satory, France, to prove that man could fly.

Ader went to the airplane and checked it over for the fiftieth time that afternoon. Its two twenty-horsepower steam engines were in perfect order, but he turned over the four-bladed propellers just to be certain. Its bat-like wings, sixty feet from tip to tip, extended away from the body of the plane.

Excitedly, Ader felt the wind slacken and steady. The sun had almost set. In another few moments it would be too

dark. It was 5:15 when Ader climbed into the plane and gunned the motors. At the last moment General Grillon climbed into the seat beside him. Tensely the other French officers and professors watched as the *Avion* started downwind.

Gradually it picked up speed. With difficulty, Ader held the airplane on an even keel with the wheel at the rear that was used for steering.

The electrician-aviator was in trouble now. The *Avion* was not traveling fast enough. The School of Musketry, with its posts and barriers, was approaching him at an alarming rate. Ader pushed the throttle full on.

Suddenly, the rear wheel rose from the ground and then the whole plane. But the posts ahead were dangerously close. Ader cut off the steam and the *Avion* landed on its nose in a splintering crash, damaged beyond repair.

Did the *Avion* really fly? Or was it picked up by the gusty twilight wind? Ader, unhurt by the accident, claimed that it flew and gave this account of the flight:

"We started off at a lively pace. In keeping the *Avion* on the white line I had much difficulty, for the wind was still blowing quite strongly and across our path. Finally a harder blow caused the machine to drift to one side, though still traveling forward. I immediately put over the rudder to the left as far as it would go, at the same time increasing the steam pressure, in order to regain our course. But the wind was too much for the *Avion;* it drifted farther and farther away from the mark, and began running toward the School of Musketry. Frightened at the prospect of the machine striking the posts and barriers guarding the School, and surprised to find the wheels of the machine lifting off the ground, I hastily shut off steam and stopped the engine. Then came a great shock, a splintering, a heavy concussion, and we were in the midst of the wrecked machine."

What of the five witnesses who saw the "flight"? They were in complete disagreement. General Grillon, who had also climbed from the wreckage uninjured, claimed that the *Avion* flew. General Mensier said it made a few hops like a grasshopper. Thereupon the two military leaders engaged in a sarcastic exchange which did more to end their former friendship than to determine whether the airplane had been invented.

Lieutenant Binet, the other officer, managed to escape the wrangle between his superiors when he joined the two professors from the Polytechnical School, Messrs. Sarran and Lente. All three avoided the main issue and agreed that the *Avion* was "apparently capable of flight."

History determined the issue for them. It became apparent that the steam engine was too heavy, the wings, though flexible at Ader's will, were not adjustable enough to maintain control, nor was the craft stable enough to remain in the air. Consequently history has recorded Ader's short hops as "promising early experiments [that] did not qualify as sustained flights."

Ader's was the last real attempt to use steam as a source of power. His failure and the failure of Sir Hiram Maxim had demonstrated that steam power was too heavy to maintain a flying machine in the air.

Success or failure, Clement Ader is remembered fondly by all Frenchmen, and an airplane is to them *un avion* today. The original *Avion* was placed in the Arts and Handicrafts Museum in Paris and there it remained until 1908 when it was transferred to the Aeronautical Salon to take its place with other famous airplanes that followed it.

27: FAILURE

THE story of Dr. Samuel Pierpont Langley and his aerodromes, or "air runners," is one of failure. But it is a story of patience, and of a failure that almost became a story of success.

Like Sir Hiram Maxim and Octave Chanute, Dr. Langley was past his youth when he became interested in heavier-than-air craft. Like Maxim, he decided that it was not necessary for him to learn to glide before he flew. That was his fatal mistake. If he had followed the lead of Octave Chanute, as the Wright brothers did, his failure might have turned into success.

Dr. Langley was born in Roxbury, Massachusetts, in 1834. He was first an architect, but later became an assistant at the

Harvard Observatory. There he studied mathematics and physics, and became an assistant professor at Annapolis, then a professor at the Western University of Pennsylvania. It was not until 1886 that he began the active study of aerodynamics. A year later he took a position as assistant secretary of the Smithsonian Institution in Washington, D. C.

Again following the lead of Sir Hiram Maxim, Dr. Langley constructed a whirling boom to test his airfoil sections and model planes. The wind tunnel had not found its way to America, but his centrifugal arm served the same purpose. Powered by steam, the tip of the arm traveled at the rate of seventy miles an hour. On it he mounted bird wings and attached his models.

In 1890 Dr. Langley was promoted and became secretary of the Smithsonian Institution. His new position left him more time to devote to his studies.

Then followed hundreds of tiny models powered with rubber bands, a method Dr. Langley had learned from Alphonse Pénaud's experiments. But Dr. Langley was not satisfied. The flights were short and unpredictable, and did not convince him that his theories were properly tested.

He began to make, in 1891, larger models, fourteen feet or more in span, and driven by real power. He called each of these models aerodromes, and he constructed five in as many years, before he met with any success. His last flew for six seconds!

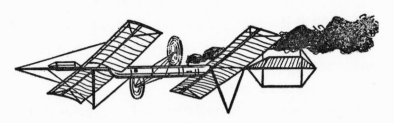

Dr. Langley's Steam Model – 1896

Dr. Langley possessed the virtue of patience. It was rewarded by his sixth and seventh aerodromes, which were larger than the others. They were to be tested together and launched from a catapult at the shore of the Potomac River. The former nosed up, stalled, and fell into the water, but the latter rose easily and securely and flew three complete circles, a distance of thirty-two hundred feet. Alexander Graham Bell watched the performance, and it may have been then, on May 6, 1896, that a spark was kindled in the mind of that great inventor which led him to ambitious experiments. Unfortunately, they too were destined to be unsuccessful.

Later in 1896 the seventh aerodrome made a longer flight over the Potomac, a distance of forty-two hundred feet and at a speed of thirty miles an hour.

Dr. Samuel P. Langley was attracting public attention now and, with it, public scorn. Why was the secretary of the National Museum wasting his time with such contraptions? His was a dignified and sober position and Dr. Langley was not acting the part.

In spite of the ridicule there were those who believed in Dr. Langley, and this was his moment of triumph. If he had stopped in 1896 and turned his attention in other directions, the fickle public might have turned from ridicule to acclaim.

But Dr. Langley was caught in a web of his own design. The war with Spain was upon us, and one of Dr. Langley's co-workers, Charles D. Walcott, sent a confidential message to President McKinley. The President was quick to communicate with the young Assistant Secretary of the Navy, Theodore Roosevelt, and before Dr. Langley knew it he was explaining the details of his craft to the military establishment. Congress voted fifty thousand dollars to build a man-carrying aerodrome for the armed services.

Dr. Langley realized the task that confronted him, but accepted it with confidence. His greatest difficulty lay in finding a suitable power plant for his plane. He had used steam and carbonic gas motors on his models and they had developed up to one horsepower. But they were too heavy. He decided to try the new gasoline engine.

"I will need a motor that will weigh not over a hundred pounds, but which will develop twelve horsepower," Dr. Langley said, and tried to place his order with one of the companies now manufacturing horseless carriages.

"Impossible," they said, laughing at his eccentricity.

Undiscouraged, Dr. Langley sent his assistant, Charles M. Manly, to Europe to find the motor there.

Manly returned only to report that his requests had been turned away with scorn. But Charles M. Manly was one of those who believed in Dr. Langley.

"Let me try it," he begged. "It is our last chance."

Dr. Langley agreed. There was nothing else that could be done.

Charles M. Manly was not an experienced machinist, and the difficulties that beset him were gargantuan. But one by one he overcame them. He made his own spark plugs, his own ignition system. He abandoned the old line-type motor and arranged his cylinders in a circle, creating the world's first radial engine. When he was finished the result startled even Manly himself.

The engine weighed 125 pounds, 25 pounds more than the specifications called for. But it produced 52.4 horsepower— 2.4 pounds per horsepower and 3.6 pounds with radiator and gas tank. It was an engine not again equaled in fourteen years.

In the meantime Dr. Langley had been at work on the full-sized aerodrome. Its monoplane wings were mounted one behind the other in tandem fashion, their span forty-eight feet. A pronounced dihedral angle was to keep the ship stable laterally, and to keep it straight in the air Dr. Langley borrowed another idea from Alphonse Pénaud: a tail with a horizontal pivot set at a slight angle.

Ship and engine were joined and with Charles Manly

aboard weighed altogether 750 pounds. It was an impressive looking craft, and both Dr. Langley and Manly were eager for the trials.

Unfortunately it was here that Dr. Langley's faulty belief took over. If Dr. Langley had learned to glide first, it is unlikely that he would have chosen a houseboat in the Potomac River as a launching site, nor a catapult as launching method. He would have realized that flying speed was an essential to success. He would have preferred a more conventional take-off run to gain that speed. He would have mistrusted the tricky mechanism of a catapult. Dr. Langley's tide of good fortune had run out.

The test was set for October 7, 1903. The aerodrome was hoisted to the top of the houseboat and made fast to the catapult. Charles Manly climbed abroad, the two propellers just behind the front wing whirred a foot from Manley's head, a thousand turns a minute.

The heavy rope was cut. Huge coil springs were released. The aerodrome hurtled forward.

A release pin failed to function, a post was pulled sideways and struck a wing.

The aerodrome reached the end of the catapult and slumped into the waters of the Potomac.

Newspapers the country over poured ridicule and derision on Dr. Langley and Mr. Manly, but they suffered in silence, still believing in their invention. They grappled it from the river's bottom, repaired it, and announced that a second trial would take place on December 8, 1903.

Again the aerodrome was made ready. Again reporters and photographers were assembled, and again Charles Manly, none the worse for his first experience, took the controls. At 4:45 in the afternoon the heavy rope was again cut and the aerodrome was on its way. And again failure cast its black shadow over the ill-fated plane.

A guidepost dragged and struck the rear wing. The aerodrome nosed into the air and fell tail first into the water.

This time the newspapers were merciless. They clamored for a congressional investigation and deplored the wasting of public funds for such useless contraptions. The government, although its official reports blamed the launching device, declined further money for more experiments. Dr. Langley and Charles Manly, again fortunate to have climbed unhurt from the wreckage, were forced to abandon their work.

Dr. Langley died in 1906, his heart broken by the adverse opinion of the public. It is sad to know that he died without realizing that his name would go down as one of the great pioneers in aviation and that it would be remembered with the names of Chanute, and Ader, and Pilcher, and the others.

It is sad to realize that he died without knowing that one day in 1914 his aerodrome would be rebuilt by another pioneer, Glenn Curtiss, and although its wings were not as good as they had been, and the years had reduced its engine from fifty-two to thirty-five horsepower, the aerodrome took off under its own reduced power and flew!

It rests now in its original state in the National Museum at Washington, D. C.

If Dr. Samuel P. Langley had learned to glide, he would never have used a catapult. Without the defective catapult he might have attained the success on the Potomac on December 8, 1903, that was for him so near and yet so far away.

For, nine days later, in an obscure part of North Carolina called Kill Devil Hill, man won the struggle that he had carried on for so many years.

Nine days later, at Kitty Hawk, man conquered the air!

28: HOPE

MANY of the early pioneers had spent their lives searching and testing and trying to fly. Some met with limited success and added their bit of progress to the struggle with the sky.

With the help of those who had gone before them it took the Wright brothers four years to complete the conquest.

Not that Wilbur Wright and Orville, his younger brother, had not always been interested in aviation. While they were children, their father, the Reverend Milton Wright, bishop of the United Brethren of Christ, had brought a toy helicopter to them at their home in Dayton, Ohio. Eagerly they had twisted its propeller and rubber band and, with their sister Katherine, watched it climb time and time again to

161

the ceiling. When its fragile framework was worn out, they had whittled new ones which had flown even higher.

An era of kite flying followed, and then the interest was set aside by the more pressing problems of manhood. If it had not been for two illnesses, the conquest of the air might have been left to others.

The first illness was that of Wilbur, and because of it he decided not to go to Yale University. When he had recovered he opened, instead, a small bicycle repair shop with his brother, in Dayton. As bicycling was at the height of its popularity, their business prospered and soon the brothers were manufacturing a wheel called "Van Cleve" which sold rapidly through their native state.

The second illness fell to Orville in 1896. It was typhoid fever, and during his long convalescence Wilbur, who was devoted to his brother, read to him. One evening, while he was reading the *Telegraphic News,* he came across a small item relating the death of Otto Lilienthal, in Germany. The brothers started a discussion of gliders that lasted far into the night.

The next day Wilbur went to his home library and reread Professor Étienne Marey's *Animal Mechanism,* a book which had been published in 1873.

Discussion followed discussion. At first the brothers began the study as a sport to occupy their leisure time. It soon took on a more serious aspect. In time they had read, studied, and discussed everything on flight that was available to them.

It was in 1899 that they decided they must do something about it. They had begun!

Few brothers worked so well together. Indeed few remarkable inventions are ever equally credited to two persons. But the Wright brothers were the exception that proved the rule.

Together they decided that Maxim, Ader, and Langley were mistaken in applying power without learning first to glide. They preferred to follow the reasoning of Lilienthal, Pilcher, and Chanute. But by their own calculations Lilienthal, the master, had only the experience of five hours flying time, spread out in ten-second bits over five years. How could they improve on his methods?

The answer, they felt, was to build a glider, but to fly it like a kite. They could go aloft in that, and its rope leash would replace the motor. It would stay aloft for hours and give them all the practical experience they needed. The brothers built a small five-foot model to see if their plan might work. The model flew.

Again they discussed the problem and decided to build a kite-glider that would stay aloft in a wind blowing eighteen miles an hour. That should be enough to carry a man safely into the air. Where would they find steady winds of that velocity? A letter was dispatched to the weather bureau, and the reply advised them: "Go to Kitty Hawk, North Carolina."

In 1900 the craft was built, packed, and shipped. Leaving their business with a trusted employee, Charles Taylor, the brothers were on their way.

Kitty Hawk was a bleak and desolate place: a few fishermen's shanties, sand dunes, and the Atlantic Ocean. There, near twin sand dunes called Kill Devil Hills, the brothers pitched a tent and began to construct a crude workshop. When the glider arrived in October they assembled it and covered the wings.

It was a disappointment. Its wing area was 165 feet, but its lifting capacity even in winds much higher than eighteen miles an hour was woefully inadequate. It would carry nei-

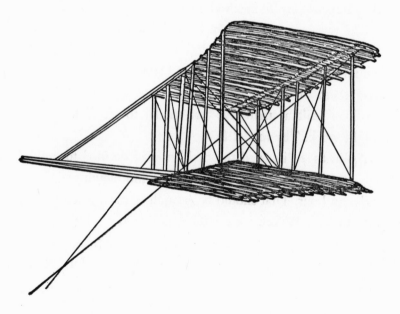

ther of them aloft, and they were forced to fly it unmanned and to work the controls by means of cords pulled from the ground.

Their first trip to Kitty Hawk was not in vain, however. They learned that their system of controls would work. Months before, they had decided that the body-twisting motions of Lilienthal were not for them and that some other means must be devised. True, Chanute had approached the problem, but he too had been forced to rely for the most part on shifting the weight of the pilot. What could be done?

The answer had come to Wilbur in the bicycle shop one day just after he had delivered an inner tube to a customer. He had waited with the cardboard box top in his hands, twisting it idly while the customer made a painstaking inspection of the tube. The twisted top! If the wing could be warped, one edge down, the other up, would not the airflow over the twisted wings solve their problems?

Orville agreed to try it, and the earliest aileron was born.

The second glider in 1901 was larger, 308 square feet in its wings, and had an elevator added to the front. Skids were placed below, adequate to land on the sandy shore.

This time the glider would carry a man aloft. It did not fly well, the Wrights knew that, but it did manage to get into the air—as a kite. They were pleased, yet puzzled. They were pleased because they learned that they could control the direction of their kite by means of its controls, and that it

165

was no longer necessary to shift their weight when flying. But they were puzzled because so many of their calculations concerning lift and resistance and pressures were wrong.

Back home in Dayton they compared the tables they had been using with others and found that each of them was different. Some had to be wrong. They must make their own tables, their own calculations.

At first they placed tiny fans on the front of their bicycles and pumped madly over the streets of Dayton. Because word of their experiments had leaked out, they were jeered at by people who thought they were trying to fly, and they good-naturedly retired to their bicycle shop. This time they built a small wind tunnel, and in it they tested some two hundred metal wing sections.

In 1902 they were back at Kitty Hawk for the third summer. Octave Chanute visited them frequently and his assistant, Augustus Herring, who had worked so long with Lilienthal, was with him. A movable rudder was added to give lateral control. By the end of the year they had made a thousand glides, some lasting sixty seconds and covering as long a distance as six hundred feet. What was more, the gliders were no longer flown at the end of ropes, but had been cast free over the sloping sands. When they returned to Dayton, the Wright brothers were ready to add power to a new "Wright Flier."

At once they encountered more problems. The first was

a motor. They did not know that Dr. Langley was having the same trouble as they. The automobile manufacturers could not, or would not, build an engine for them. Wilbur and Orville, with the help of Charles Taylor, constructed a compact four-cylinder gasoline engine in six weeks. It was heavier than Langley's, 250 pounds, and it developed only twelve horsepower, though by later tinkering it was increased to sixteen.

The next problem was the propeller. There was little or no information available, but the brothers carved one after lengthy tests with their wind tunnel. They figured it would be 66 per cent efficient, far better than others of its time.

How could they overcome torque, the twisting operation of the whirling blade so likely to throw the airplane into a spin? They solved this problem quickly by carving a second propeller. The pair, attached behind the wings of their biplane and driven by sprockets and chains, revolved in opposite directions.

The motor was mounted in the new glider in such a position that it would not strike the pilot if it were thrown forward in a crash landing. As in some of the older machines, the pilot lay prone in the body of the plane and worked the controls by means of a yoke on his shoulders. The newer craft was restrengthened, especially in the wings.

In September 1903 the new machine was shipped to Kitty Hawk.

During preliminary tests all kinds of delays beset the inventors, fortunately most of them minor. Power shafts broke and Orville was forced to return to Dayton for new ones. The sprockets had a disconcerting way of sliding off the rods until Wilbur finally melted a batch of bicycle tire cement and poured it on. A hurricane threatened, but with ropes and shutters the workshop was battened down and the danger averted.

On December 14, 1903, all was ready. All, that is, except the wind. It was too low for a level start. The plane would not gather enough speed. The brothers raised the launching track to the side of a hill.

A coin was tossed and Wilbur won.

Before the plane had left the track a landing skid broke and a wing tip was broken.

Three days passed before the repairs were completed, late in the evening of December 16, 1903.

Tomorrow it would be Orville's turn.

29: SUCCESS

ORVILLE WRIGHT gazed out from the window of the crude work shed. Outside, the wind was whipping up the waves on the edge of the Atlantic Ocean, and beyond the rolling surf whitecaps seemed to cover the water. A small handmade anemometer registered the strength of the wind at twenty-seven miles an hour.

It was Monday, December 17, 1903.

It was cold, and in spite of the wind which had howled all the night before, the puddles near the entrance to the shed were covered with ice. Inside, the wood fire that burned vigorously in the old carbide can felt comfortable, but Orville had no desire that morning to remain within the circle of its warmth.

169

FROM KITE TO KITTY HAWK

Today it was his turn to try to fly!

The greased runway, all sixty feet of it, had been prepared the night before. The wind had stiffened before then and the brothers had placed the track on level ground instead of down the slope of the dune. The wind itself, without the help of gravity, should give their plane the desired lift.

All of the local people for five or six miles about had been invited to witness the trial, but only five had braved the icy blasts. Orville knew them all. There was a friend, John T. Daniels, who had been interested for so long and who had helped them so often. Another friend, A. D. Etheridge, had come from the Kitty Hawk Coast Guard Station. W. S. Dough, W. C. Brinkley, and John Ward were the others.

Everything was in readiness. Orville shrugged into the heavy jacket. With Wilbur and the others he hauled the heavy airplane out of the shed, sliding it on its sled-like runners.

It was a crude affair, a biplane, its wings spanning more than thirty feet. It was like their 1902 glider, but stronger and heavier to accommodate the added weight of the motor. Twin elevators extended in front of the craft, and the hinged rudder, developed the year before, was at the rear. The motor was installed flat on its side, and drove the two propellers in opposite directions by means of bicycle chains and sprockets. The motor turned its shaft 1090 times a minute, which was much too fast, so the smaller sprocket was located there, and the larger at the hub of the propeller, gearing the big blades down to about three hundred fifty revolutions per minute. The propellers turned behind the airplane's wings.

Orville took his place, lying flat on the bottom wing of the plane beside the engine. For several minutes, while the motor warmed, Wilbur steadied the wing-tip, and balanced it on the rail.

Orville gave the signal. The rope was cut. The airplane started down the runway, Wilbur running alongside.

Orville saw that Wilbur was shouting. His lips formed the words "Good luck!" But Orville could not hear the words. They were drowned out by the roar of the motor, the clanking of chains, and the whine of the propellers. Forty feet of the track slid beneath him. Then quickly his attention was diverted to more important things.

He was airborne!

The airplane climbed easily to a height of ten feet, but suddenly darted toward the ground. Orville frantically worked the elevator's controls which were attached to a yoke on his shoulders. The airplane began to rise again. It had not touched the ground.

Three seconds, four seconds. Was the ship just gliding? Orville held his breath.

Five, six, seven seconds . . . The plane flew on. It must

be flying under its own power! It must be! It was staying up, not coming down!

Ten seconds . . . The plane still flew. Orville nosed it down now, picking a smooth place to land. The plane bumped and slid on the sand, just as the twelfth second had passed. One hundred and twenty feet behind him was the end of the rail. There was no doubt. The airplane had flown.

To convince the onlookers that their imaginations were not playing tricks on them, each of the brothers flew the airplane twice that day. When the sun was low on the horizon, Wilbur Wright, on the fourth and last flight, had made the longest trip by airplane in the history of man—852 feet in fifty-nine seconds.

Then, as the Wright brothers and their five enthusiastic friends were about to return the airplane to its shed, the gusty wind, as if recognizing defeat but striking its last forceful blow, upended the airplane. John T. Daniels, the huskiest of the spectators, grabbed at a wing and with the inventors tried to save the craft, but he was tumbled over and over with it. He laughed off his bruises, but none of the men at Kitty Hawk could laugh off the damage to the plane.

It was shipped off to Dayton, never to fly again. It had done its work and had done it well. The spectators had seen it and the Wrights' camera had recorded its achievements.

That night Orville reminded Wilbur of the dollar that

their father, Bishop Wright, had given them for a telegram. If they had good news they were to let him know.

The dispatcher at Kitty Hawk was none too accurate, but the telegram was nonetheless effective:

"SUCCESS FOUR FLIGHTS THURSDAY MORNING ALL AGAINST TWENTY ONE MILE WIND STARTED FROM LEVEL WITH ENGINE POWER ALONE AVERAGE SPEED THROUGH AIR THIRTY ONE MILES LONGEST 57 SECONDS INFORM PRESS HOME CHRISTMAS

OREVELLE WRIGHT"

Only a few reporters ran the story in their papers, some skeptical, others fanciful. It was more than four years before the world as a whole believed that man had conquered the skies.

With the achievement of the Wright brothers, an era ended, the era of the invention of the airplane. There was another period to come, a period of development, testing, and improvement. But the conquest was over.

Man-made steppingstones had reached into the sky!

30: AFTERMATH

DURING the next two or three years most of the flying done was by the Wright brothers. It was not until September 15, 1905, that Orville made the first turn in the air, and on the 20th that Wilbur turned the first circle. They continued their experiments quietly and cautiously, but gradually the world came to believe in their feats of magic. In 1906 a patent was granted to them for their wing-warping, their elevators, and their rudder—the method of control which had enabled them to succeed where others had failed.

Aviation began to develop, slowly at first, and then with a rapidity that made even the most skeptical gasp.

Some pioneers continued to work with gliders. Professor John J. Montgomery of Santa Clara College was one. As far back as 1883 he had claimed to be the first American to glide, and later had built several ships.

On April 25, 1905, a famous parachutist, S. M. Maloney, cut loose from a balloon at almost four thousand feet and flew a Montgomery glider to the ground. Maloney accomplished the feat fifty times in the next three months, but was killed July 18, 1905, when he tried it once again. Professor Montgomery gave his own life in 1911, when one of his gliders crashed at San Jose, California. Gliders bowed to their powered brothers and became only the sport of hardy adventurers seeking a thrill.

Alberto Santos-Dumont, who had thrilled the multitudes with his exploits in lighter-than-air craft, was converted to powered airplanes, and continued to entertain spectators with his feats of daring and to hold other aviators in awe of his technical skill.

In 1907 Henri C. Farman, of France, added the first wheels to an airplane and became a leading manufacturer; in 1909 Glenn Curtiss, an American already on his road to fame, established a speed record of forty-six miles an hour in sustained flight, and on July 25, 1909, Louis Blériot made his famous thirty-seven-minute English Channel flight.

The pioneering days of aviation were coming to a close. World War I jumped the progress of aviation years ahead of its time in nations all over the world. The prone position had long before given way to the bucket seat, and that to

Blériot's English Channel Flight – 1909

the open cockpit. Spads, Nieuports, Fokkers, DeHavilands,
Curtiss planes were turned out in large numbers. The OX
motor, the in-line workhorse of early aviation, and the rotary
engine gave way to the radial engine.

After the war aviation became a business. It developed in
a serious way with the flight of the NC4 across the Atlantic
in 1919; it also developed in a barnstorming way, when pilots,

both ex-military and civilian, bought, borrowed, or built "flying crates," kept them patched with bits of canvas and haywire and offered rides to John Q. Public from local hayfields at ten dollars a ride.

In 1921 James H. Knight, later the famous "Jack" Knight, began to fly a division on the first transcontinental airmail. Two years later John A. Macready and Oakley Kelly, on their third attempt, made the first coast-to-coast nonstop flight, and when a leak developed in the line of their water-cooled motor near the end of their flight, they kept their staggering craft in the air by pouring coffee into the radiator.

In 1923, also, Juan de la Cierva flew his first autogyro, a combination of airplane and helicopter that was to be improved by Pitcairn in this country, and to increase in popularity in the next decade, only to give way to the modern helicopter.

General Billy Mitchell tried to convince the military of the importance of the airplane, and dared speak out over the objections of his superiors. He was court-martialed and resigned in 1926, to be posthumously awarded the Congressional Medal of Honor when his predictions proved true.

The struggle with the Atlantic was won by the Lone Eagle, Charles A. Lindbergh, on May 20, 1927, when he soloed the *Spirit of St Louis* from New York to Paris. Others tried the feat, Clarence Chamberlain, Ruth Elder, Amelia Earhart, Richard E. Byrd with Bernt Balchen, Bert Acosta and George O. Noville, Russell Boardman, John Polando, Douglas Corrigan and many others, with varying degrees of success.

The Pacific was also a challenge, and on May 31, 1928, Sir Charles Kingsford-Smith and Captain Charles T. P. Ulm met the challenge with a flight from the United States to Australia.

For a time the dirigibles, the "flying elephants," tried to hold their own, their advantage lying in the number of passengers they could carry. Count Ferdinand von Zeppelin provided basic plans until his death in 1917, and his work was carried on by others. Dr. Hugo Eckener was the most noted of these, and not only took over management of the Zeppelin enterprises in 1921, but became the world's greatest pilot of the huge craft. The *Los Angeles,* the *Graf Zeppelin,* the *Hindenburg* were developed, piloted by him. In America the huge ships *Shenandoah, Akron,* and *Macon* were constructed. But one by one they crashed, or burned, or proved to be unfit for use. The flying elephants lost the struggle and became memories of the past. The balloon was relegated to meteorological use, a device for high altitude flights, or a captive thing to harass enemy military craft.

The span of the world itself was the next distance to tempt fliers. Jules Verne's *Around the World in Eighty Days* passed from fantasy to reality to quaintness. John Mears and Charles B. D. Collyer flew around the earth in a few hours over twenty-three days in 1928. The U. S. Army had flown a fleet commanded by Col. Lowell H. Smith around the globe in 1924. Wiley Post and Harold Gatty, flying the *Winnie Mae,* made the trip in eight days in 1933. In 1937 America's sweetheart of the air, Amelia Earhart, made the attempt. Idol of millions, she and her navigator, Fred Noonan, were forced down and lost in the broad waters of the Pacific Ocean.

The air over the North and South poles alone remained unflown territory. The North was quickly invaded by Roald Amundsen and Lincoln Ellsworth in 1925, and the South by Richard E. Byrd, Bernt Balchen, and Harold June in 1929.

Flights of long duration became the vogue, and in 1929 General Ira C. Eaker piloted the *Question Mark,* commanded by General Carl Spaatz, for 150 hours and 40 minutes, refueling in the air. Aviation had traveled quite a distance since the first twelve-second flight twenty-six years before.

Aircraft had developed speed as well. Roscoe Turner, Alford Williams, and James H. Doolittle pushed the records higher and higher until in 1932 "Jimmy" Doolittle held the landplane speed record of 296 miles an hour.

As an instrument of good will, the airplane flew mass flights or single missions to nations all over the world. Italo Balbo, in 1933, commanded a mass flight from Italy to the Chicago Century of Progress Exposition. Captain James A. Mollison and his wife, Amy, flew over much of the world, as did Charles A. Lindbergh and his wife, Anne. These flights and many others did much to cement international relationships and to bring realization that the world was rapidly shrinking in size.

On September 30, 1929, Fritz von Opel of Germany flew the first jet reaction airplane powered by rockets. Captain Frank Whittle in 1930 invented a true jet engine which was flown in an airplane in 1941. An entire new era in aviation was about to begin.

Like World War I, the second world explosion brought a rapid advance in flying. The oceans were minor obstacles now and huge bombers were ferried "across the pond" in routine fashion. The Mustang reached 450 miles per hour. The Flying Fortress and its successors flew long-range missions in huge mass flights.

These were just a few of the events that marked man's first fifty years in the air. A thousand volumes have been written describing his early fledgling flights and his later exploits in the air. The task of keeping this record up to date we leave to those who have done it so well in the past and will do it so well again. This is the story of man's conquest of the air, not of his exploration of the new element after he had conquered it.

31: TODAY . . .
AND TOMORROW

UNTIL the development of the jets man had simply used the Wright brothers' basic ideas and had improved on them. With jet propulsion, at the end of World War II, a whole new vista was open.

Scientists who had solemnly declared that an airplane would burn when it reached the sound barrier were proved wrong.

Commercial aviation was rapidly overtaking the railroad in passenger totals, and in 1954, for the first time, there were more air passengers than railroad coach passengers in the United States. Instead of a solitary flight across the Atlantic now and then, it is estimated that half a million people crossed the ocean by air in 1953. During 1955 the world's domestic and international airlines carried nearly fifty-two million passengers. A domestic scheduled aircraft took off or landed about once every seven seconds.

It is almost useless to quote figures of today's aircraft. Between the time they are written and the time you read them, they will be obsolete. But here are a few anyway:

Lieutenant Colonel Marion E. Carl, piloting a D558 II Skyrocket, launched at 34,000 feet from a B-29, climbed to an altitude of 83,235 feet; Scott Crossfield, piloting a Douglas Skyrocket, reached a speed of 1327 miles an hour; TWA inaugurated a scheduled nonstop coast-to-coast air service, scheduled for eight to nine hours each way, and a little over a month later American Airlines started a similar service; a Navy jet flew across country, west to east, in 3 hours, 23 minutes, 8.4 seconds.

In January 1955, a Stratojet, unable to land in a flight between England and North Africa, refueled in the air and stayed aloft for over 47 hours, flying 21,000 miles to set a new jet endurance record. Jacqueline Cochran became the first woman to fly faster than the speed of sound. In 1956 a Bell X-2 rocket plane manned by Captain Milburn G. Apt flew about 2200 miles an hour at an altitude of 126,000 feet. At the same time a helicopter made the first nonstop flight across the United States.

It's a bold author indeed who dares make "predictions of things to come" when feats such as these have been accom-

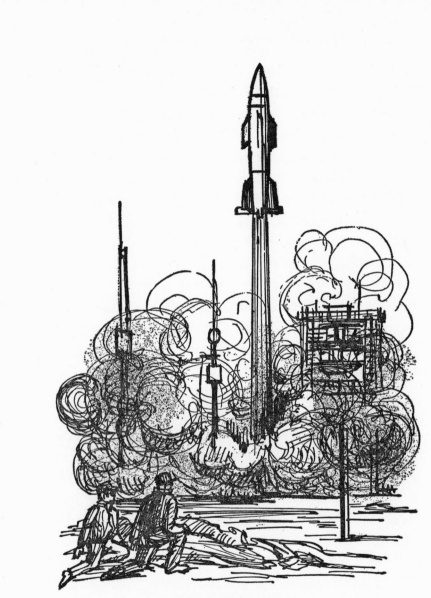

A Guided Missile Test

plished in the short space of fifty years. Consider, however, that aviation is still in its infancy. What will the future hold?

Ideas have changed. Talk of flight in space no longer surprises or terrifies the public. Scientists who were so cautious before not only admit the possibility, but foresee it as a fact in days to come. They no longer worry about the heat of friction burning plane and pilot to a crisp at the speed of sound. They are more concerned with the problems and difficulties which may take place as aircraft approach the speed of light.

The scientists are also more concerned with how to control the "sonic boom," the shock wave that sounds like thunder and that is produced by jets flying faster than the speed of sound. They are more concerned in testing the number of "G's," the measure of gravity pull that a human body can stand.

Guided missiles with automatic radar homing devices, robot airplanes, flying platforms, one-man strap-on helicopters are being tested and used. Satellites, circling the earth in their own orbits each ninety minutes at speeds up to 18,000 miles an hour, have become a reality. Trips by human beings to the moon and back have been variously predicted within two to twenty years.

Flying saucers are the subject of discussion among engineers and among men on the street today. Man-made? Illusions? Interplanetary space-craft? The last suggestion does not seem half so far-fetched as it might have been a few years ago. After eight years of investigation, the U.S. Air Force in the fall of 1955 denied the existence of flying saucers, and in the same breath announced that the Air Force was about to fly a jet-powered vertical-rising airplane, and that a disk-shaped airplane was being made under a new contract.

Some day man will conquer space. Have no doubt about it. At our scientific museums visitors are already signing up for the first trip to Mars.

Aviation today is only a little more than fifty years old. If the same amount of progress is made in the next half century, man's conquest of the sky may exceed our most fantastic dreams.

Stepping Stones to the Sky

The chapters of this book have traced the main steps in the pathway of man's conquest of the air. But in between these major achievements in the struggle were countless minor advances, each contributing its bit toward ultimate victory.

Needless to say it would be impossible to list or to describe every contribution made by man. They are too many. Here, however, exclusive of myth and legend, are a few of those events that helped man to progress along the pathway into the air above:

B.C.

150   HERO is credited with discovering the principles of jet propulsion.

A.D.

1250 * ROGER BACON wrote that a properly designed flying machine could be built to float in the air.

* Approximate date.

187

FROM KITE TO KITTY HAWK

1483 * LEONARDO DA VINCI conducted experiments and research in the art of flying and parachuting.

1496   LEONARDO DA VINCI devised a mechanical flying machine, a parachute, and an airscrew propeller.

1640 * JOHN WILKINS, Lord Bishop of Chester, wrote *Discourse Concerning Flying,* an imaginative but impractical solution for achieving flight.

1643 * EVANGELISTA TORRICELLI discovered that earth's atmosphere was not a vacuum but was a mixture of gases.

1670 * FRANCESCO DE LANA designed but did not build a vacuum balloon. He was afraid it would be used to wage war. His design consisted of four copper spheres, a boat, and a sail.

1680   SIR ISAAC NEWTON, using principles of Hero, tried jet propulsion on a model horseless carriage.

1766   HENRY CAVENDISH, an English scientist, discovered hydrogen and proved that it was lighter than air.

1767 * JOSEPH BLACK, Scottish professor, suggested filling animal bladders with hydrogen.

1781 * TIBERIUS CAVALLO, Italian in England, filled soap bubbles with hydrogen—they floated. He failed in other attempts to discover a material strong and light enough to hold hydrogen and float through the air.

1783   June 5. ÉTIENNE and JOSEPH MONTGOLFIER demonstrated the first hot-air balloon made of linen and paper.

1783   August 27. PROFESSOR J. A. C. CHARLES sent unmanned linen balloon treated with rubber and filled with hydrogen aloft to a height of three thousand feet and distance of fifteen miles.

1783   September 19. ÉTIENNE and JOSEPH MONTGOLFIER sent a

sheep, a duck, and a rooster aloft in a hot-air balloon at Versailles, France. The flight was witnessed by Benjamin Franklin.

1783   October 15. JEAN JACQUES PILÂTRE DE ROZIER was the first man to go aloft. The balloon, held down by ropes, reached a height of eighty-five feet and stayed in the air four and one-half minutes.

1783   November 21. PILÂTRE DE ROZIER and the MARQUIS D'ARLANDES made first flight in a free balloon at Paris, France. The flight lasted twenty minutes in time and five and one-half miles in distance.

1783   November 25. Italian COUNT FRANCESCO ZAMBECARRI made first balloon flight in England, forty-eight miles, two and one-half hours.

1783   December 1. PROFESSOR J. A. C. CHARLES, accompanied by one of the Roberts brothers, made flight in hydrogen-filled Charlière, first to use barometer, ballast, and valve, to record and control their craft.

1783   LOUIS SEBASTIAN LEONORMAND jumped from observatory tower at Montpelier, France, using parachute of his own design.

1784 *   JEAN BAPTISTE MARIE MEUSNIER planned an elliptical-shaped balloon. A hand-driven propeller gave the balloon a speed of about three miles per hour.

1784   January 19. JOSEPH MONTGOLFIER, PILÂTRE DE ROZIER, and five others ascended three thousand feet in one quarter of an hour in the *Flesselles,* a large hot-air balloon.

1784   February 22. A hydrogen balloon, unmanned, crossed English Channel from Sandwich, England, to Warneton, France, a distance of seventy-five miles.

1784   February 25. CHEVALIER PAUL ANDREANI made first balloon ascension in Italy.

1784   March 2. JEAN PIERRE BLANCHARD, famous balloonist of the eighteenth century, made his first flight at Paris.

1784   April 25. GUYTON DE MORVEAU constructed balloon that made successful flight at Dijon, France. During the French Revolution de Morveau was placed in charge of a military aeronautic school founded at Mendon.

1784   April 28. LAUNOY and BIENVENU demonstrated working model of helicopter, made with feathers and springs at the French Academy of Science. This was the first heavier-than-air device to lift itself into the air.

1784   June 4. MADAME THIBLE, a Frenchwoman, became the first woman to fly. She was a passenger in a montgolfier at Lyons, France.

1784   June 24. Unconfirmed report of a balloon ascension in Baltimore, Maryland. The craft, a montgolfier, was constructed by PETER CARNES and the ascent made by a thirteen-year-old boy, EDWARD WARREN. It is suspected that the balloon was tethered by ropes.

1784   July 15. Roberts brothers ascended in first cylindrically shaped balloon at St. Cloud.

1784   August 27. JAMES TYTLER was first Englishman to make balloon flight in Great Britain, its duration only a few minutes, distance about half a mile.

1784   September 15. VINCENT LUNARDI, Secretary to the Neapolitan ambassador to Great Britain, made aerial ascent of one and one-half hours at London, England, with the King and Prince of Wales observing.

STEPPING STONES TO THE SKY

1785   January 7. DR. JOHN JEFFRIES and JEAN PIERRE BLANCHARD were first to fly across English Channel.

1790   May 31. ANDRÉ JACQUES GARNERIN, later famous as inventor of parachute, made a successful flight in a balloon of his own construction.

1793   January 9. JEAN PIERRE BLANCHARD made first authenticated ascension in United States.

1794   June 26. At the battle of Fleurs the first use was made of a balloon for military observation purposes by COLONEL JEAN MARIE JOSEPH COUTELLE.

1796   SIR GEORGE CAYLEY devised and flew Cayley's top, and began experimenting with gliders.

1797   October 22. ANDRÉ JACQUES GARNERIN made first successful parachute jump. His leap was at Paris, France, from a height of six thousand feet.

1797   JEANNE GENEVIEVE GARNERIN, wife of André Jacques Garnerin, became first woman balloon pilot. Later she was the first woman to jump with a parachute.

1798   PIERRE TESTU-BRISSY, exhibition balloonist, made an ascent on horseback. The horse had been trained to stand on a platform suspended below the balloon.

1802   September 21. ANDRÉ JACQUES GARNERIN made his second successful parachute jump from a balloon, the first jump in England.

1809   The first of SIR GEORGE CAYLEY's articles on "Aerial Navigation" appeared in *Nicholson's Journal*. The three articles of 1809–1810 were the first scientific treatment of the principles of aviation.

1817   WINDHAM SADLER was first to cross the Irish Sea by balloon.

1821   July 19. CHARLES GREEN, famous English aeronaut, flew his *Coronation Balloon* at Green Park, London, during coronation of George IV, the first balloon to use coal gas for inflation.

1825   EDMOND CHARLES GENÊT, an immigrant from France, was granted the first aeronautical patent in the United States. The patent was signed by John Quincy Adams and Henry Clay. Although proposed to raise canal boats, its design became the basis for later airships.

1830   September 9. CHARLES FERSON DURANT became first American balloonist in United States. His flight was for two hours from Castle Garden, N. Y., to South Amboy, N. J.

1835   April 8. RICHARD CLAYTON, a young English watchmaker who had settled in Cincinnati, Ohio, left that city by balloon and travelled three hundred and sixty miles in nine and one-half hours, landing in Virginia, the longest trip to that date.

1835   May 2. JOHN WISE, famous American aeronaut, made his first ascension at Philadelphia.

1836 *   JULES DUPUIS DELCOURT, France, invented a leather-covered balloon.

1836   November 7. The *Nassau* balloon made its famous five-hundred-mile flight from London to German Duchy of Nassau, eighteen hours in the air. Constructed by CHARLES GREEN, it was flown by him and by Robert Holland, M.P., and Monck Mason. Green also invented the trailing guide rope to save gas, and the idea of ballast.

1843   SIR GEORGE CAYLEY designed a helicopter with twin rotating vanes.

1843   March 24. WILLIAM S. HENSON incorporated the Aerial Transit Company, intended to carry passengers by air with his flying machine *Ariel*.

1843   March 24. WILLIAM S. HENSON invented steam-powered monoplane, which, when tested, never managed to fly.

1846   HENRY TRACY COXWELL established a magazine *The Balloon*, the first paper of its kind devoted solely to flying.

1847   July 6. HENRY TRACY COXWELL, RICHARD GYPSON, and two others made a balloon ascension in England, carrying fireworks. They were caught in a thunderstorm and escaping gas collapsed the bag into the net holding it. The group descended by means of the resulting parachute and were unhurt.

1848   JOHN STRINGFELLOW successfully flew a small steam-powered model, the first airplane to fly under its own power.

1849   October 7. FRANCISQUE ARBAN, French aeronaut, crossed the Alps in a balloon. The hazardous journey was made from Marseilles, France, to Turin, Italy, in eight hours.

1850 * PIERRE JULLIEN, French watchmaker, became famous aeronaut. He improved propeller and demonstrated seven-meter dirigible model at Hippodrome, Paris. A full-sized dirigible, *Le Precurseur,* although never flown, incorporated many advances used in later aircraft.

1852   September 24. HENRI GIFFARD flew the first controlled lighter-than-air craft. Powered with a steam engine, the airship flew from Paris to Trappe, a distance of seventeen miles.

1855   JEAN MARIE LEBRIS made a glide of one-eighth of a mile in a glider of his own design.

1856   LOUIS PIERRE MOUILLARD constructed an airplane based on observations of birds. His published reports from 1856 to 1891 formed a basis for later successes of Octave Chanute and others.

1858   July 17. THADDEUS SOBIESKI COULINCOURT LOWE made his first balloon ascension. Lowe later was chief aeronaut of the Army of the Potomac and an outstanding American balloonist.

1859   JOHN WISE, American balloonist, flew 1120 miles in twenty hours in a cross-country flight in the United States.

1860   SAMUEL ARCHER KING and WILLIAM BLACK took first aerial photographs from balloon over Boston. Black brought the trailing guide rope to America and during his eighty-six years became the greatest of American aeronauts.

1861   JOHN LAMOUNTAIN originated the aircraft carrier by launching observation balloons from U.S.S. *Fanny*. THADDEUS LOWE, chief aeronaut of the Army used U.S.S. *Parke Custis* in the same manner a few months later.

1862   HENRY TRACY COXWELL and JAMES GLAISHER established seven-mile altitude record in a balloon, a record unbeaten for forty years.

1863   FELIX TOURNACHON, a French photographer known as Nadar, built *Le Geant,* a huge balloon with a two-story cottage as a basket. *Le Geant* carried thirteen passengers and made many long flights.

1863   GUSTAVE DE PONTON D'AMECOURT invented steam-powered helicopter with two vertical propellers. Although too heavy to rise, its principles were used in later models after invention of the gas engine.

1864   July. EUGENE GODARD, noted French aeronaut, constructed *L'Aigle,* a fire balloon of nearly five hundred thousand cubic feet. Its first flight was from Cremorne Gardens, London.

1866   FRANCIS HERBERT WENHAM, Great Britain, founded Royal Aeronautical Society and published his famous treatise "Aerial Locomotion." Wenham invented the biplane and a light gas engine.

1867 * OTTO LILIENTHAL and his brother, Gustav, Germany, began long experiments which resulted in their mastery of gliding during the following twenty-nine years.

1868   JOHN STRINGFELLOW invented and tested a model triplane based on his earlier models and improvements by F. H. Wenham.

1870   ALPHONSE PÉNAUD used rubber bands to power a model helicopter.

1870– Besieged French forces and civilians in Paris, during the
1871   Franco-Prussian War, used sixty-five balloons to carry mail and passengers to and from the city

1871   ALPHONSE PÉNAUD, France, invented mechanical bird powered by rubber bands. In flight, this mechanical toy would rise fifteen or twenty feet and fly for about fifty feet.

1872   December 13. PAUL HAENLEIN, German engineer, at Brunn, Austria, flew first dirigible powered with internal combustion engine. He invented the semirigid frame and multiple suspended cars.

1873   ÉTIENNE JULES MAREY published *Animal Mechanism* which included a detailed study of birds in flight. The book was later used by the Wright brothers in their early experiments.

1873   JOSEPH SPIESS invented the rigid airship.

1873   CAPTAIN WASHINGTON H. DONALDSON and ALFRED FORD attempted crossing of Atlantic by balloon. Taking off from Brooklyn, N. Y., the balloon was forced down at New Canaan, Conn.

1876   ALPHONSE PÉNAUD and PAUL GAUCHOT patented an airplane design that incorporated many of the features used in modern flight.

1877   The wind tunnel was invented and placed in use by the French Army.

1877   June 29. ENRICO FORLANINI, an Italian engineer, demonstrated first model steam helicopter to actually fly. It rose about forty feet and the flight lasted twenty seconds.

1879   VICTOR TATIN, French mechanic, built a compressed-air airplane model which flew eighteen miles per hour for about one hundred feet. Tatin's other accomplishments were an ornithopter that flew sixty feet, and a barograph upon which the later altimeter was based.

1883   October 8. ALBERT TISSANDIER and his brother Gaston, France, made first flight in dirigible powered by electric motor. Average speed was 6.26 miles per hour.

1884   March 17. JOHN JOSEPH MONTGOMERY, American professor, made first glider flight in United States. The glider had two wings, each ten feet in length. Distance of glide was about one hundred feet.

1884   August 9. CHARLES RENARD and ARTHUR KREBS, France, constructed *La France,* a huge electrically powered dirigible and completed a flight from Paris to Villacoublay and and return, the first round-trip powered air flight in history.

1889   OTTO LILIENTHAL published *Bird Flight as the Basis of Aviation,* the story of how he became the first to master heavier-than-air craft in more than two thousand successful glides.

1890   LAWRENCE HARGRAVE constructed a compressed air model plane that flew 368 feet. Hargrave's studies of box kites, cellular kites, ornithopters, and airplanes, and his intense belief that man could fly contributed much to the cause of aviation.

1890   October 9. CLEMENT ADER, France, claimed to be the first to pilot a heavier-than-air craft. Powered by steam, his plane is said to have risen a few feet and stayed in the air for 150 feet. The experiment was never acknowledged as sustained flight.

1893   May. HORATIO F. PHILLIPS contributed important research with a curved wing in home-made wind tunnels. He later constructed an airplane resembling a venetian blind, which flew short distances.

1894   SIR HIRAM MAXIM built huge steam airplane with 104-foot wing-spread, and 363-horsepower motors. It was never successfully flown.

1896   PERCY S. PILCHER, Great Britain, began flights in man-carrying glider based on principles of Sir George Cayley and craft of Otto Lilienthal. He made several hundred successful glides. His glider had a span of twenty-three feet, weighed two hundred pounds, and attained a speed of twenty-five miles per hour.

1896   May 6. SAMUEL P. LANGLEY flew first steam-powered model airplane in United States. The flight was across the Potomac River, a distance of about three thousand feet.

1896   OCTAVE CHANUTE, famous American railroad engineer, conducted glider tests at Lake Michigan. He turned over the results of his research and experiments to the Wright brothers to help them with their work.

1896   August 28. DR. HANS WOLFERT, Germany, constructed and flew the dirigible *Deutschland,* the first to be powered with a gasoline motor, a Daimler four-cylinder engine which developed twelve horsepower.

1897   November 13. DAVID SCHWARZ and his wife, Melaine, invented a metal balloon, the first to fly successfully.

1898 * COUNT FERDINAND VON ZEPPELIN began experiments with rigid airships.

1900 * CAPTAIN HUGH L. WILLOUGHBY, famous American balloonist and aviator, made balloon flights over Paris. Captain Willoughby was first to use maps for navigation, altimeters, and held fourteen patents for new devices on airships and airplanes.

1900   WILBUR and ORVILLE WRIGHT conducted glider experiments at Kitty Hawk, N. C.

1900   July 2. The first Zeppelin was flown, reaching a speed of eight and one-half miles per hour over Lake Constance on German-Swiss border.

1900   October. COUNT HENRI DE LA VAULX, France, established long-distance balloon record in flight from France to Russia, 1193 miles in 35¾ hours.

STEPPING STONES TO THE SKY

1900   October 21. Trial flight of Zeppelin reaches twenty miles per hour.

1901   October. WILHELM KRESS, piano manufacturer of Austria, tried unsuccessfully to fly an explosive-powered seaplane at Lake Tullnerbach. The unfortunate plane hit a rock and sank.

1901   October 13. COUNT HENRI DE LA VAULX, France, was first to cross the Mediterranean Sea by balloon, Toulon to Algeria.

1901   October 19. ALBERTO SANTOS-DUMONT won prize for flying from take-off to and around Eiffel Tower and return, a distance of seven miles in thirty minutes.

1901–
1902   WRIGHT BROTHERS constructed and used wind tunnel to aid them in their gliding experiments.

1902   September–October. Wright brothers completed glides successfully and started work on a powered plane.

1903   May 8. PIERRE and PAUL LEBAUDY constructed the Lebaudy dirigible, the first to be propelled by gasoline motor on an air voyage. The dirigible made many successful flights and was later used for military purposes.

1903   October 7. CHARLES M. MANLEY failed in attempt to fly Samuel Langley's steam-powered aerodrome at Washington, D. C.

1903   December 17. ORVILLE WRIGHT became first man to fly a heavier-than-air craft with its own power at Kitty Hawk, N. C. Distance 120 feet; time twelve seconds.
Later on the same day WILBUR WRIGHT flew the same craft 852 feet in fifty-nine seconds.

Heroes of Experimental Flight

All of those who helped to pave the way in man's pathway into the sky contributed their time and money to the ultimate success of the conquest. A few contributed more.

Riding the skies after the Wright brothers was not always the safe adventure that it is today, and many more died in the early development of the science of flying. But here we would like to remember those who risked their lives without knowing whether their dreams would ever be fulfilled, when gliding thirty feet above the ground was more dangerous than a round-the-world trip is now.

These are the early experimenters who gave their lives that man might fly:

1785 June 15. PILÂTRE DE ROZIER and P. A. ROMAIN were the first persons to meet death when their combination hot air and hydrogen balloon exploded on an attempted flight across the English Channel.

* Approximate date.

200

HEROES OF EXPERIMENTAL FLIGHT

1837   July 24. ROBERT COCKING was killed in attempt to descend from balloon in inverted-type parachute of his own invention.

1849 *   FRANCISQUE ARBAN, French balloonist and the first to cross the Alps by air, disappeared in an attempt to fly across the Mediterranean Sea.

1874   July 5. VINCENT DE GROOF, a Belgian shoemaker, was towed aloft in a balloon and attempted to make his way to earth in a wing-flapping device. The wings collapsed and he was killed in the attempt.

1879   September 29. JOHN WISE and a companion were drowned in Lake Michigan while attempting long-distance balloon voyage.

1896   August 10. OTTO LILIENTHAL was killed at Rhinow, Germany, landing his glider after a quarter-mile flight.

1897   June 14. DR. HANS WOLFERT and his mechanic, KNABE, were killed in a crash of the dirigible *Deutschland,* Berlin, Germany.

1897   July 11. SALOMON ANDREE, NILS STRENDBERG, and KNUT FRANKEL took off in free balloon on attempted North Pole trip. Their bodies were recovered in 1930, and pictures taken by them and developed after thirty-three years told the story of their death.

1899   PERCY PILCHER, famous English expert in gliding, was killed in his craft in Great Britain.

1911   October 31. JOHN JOSEPH MONTGOMERY was killed in a fall from a glider of his own construction at San Jose, California.

1930   COUNT HENRI DE LA VAULX, holder of many lighter-than-air records, was killed in airplane crash in flight from Montreal to New York.

Bibliography

The Notebooks of Leonardo da Vinci, by Edward MacCurdy, George Braziller, Inc., New York, 1954.

Classic Myths in English Literature and in Art, by Charles Mills Gayley, Ginn and Company, Boston, 1939.

The Mind of Leonardo da Vinci, by Edward MacCurdy, Dodd, Mead & Company, New York, 1948.

The Age of Fable, by Thomas Bulfinch.

Encyclopaedia Britannica, Encyclopaedia Britannica, Inc., Chicago, 1951.

National Aircraft Collection, Smithsonian Institution, Washington, D.C., 1941.

Popular Mechanics Aviation Album, by Edward L. Throm and James S. Crenshaw, Popular Mechanics Press, Chicago, 1953.

On the Wing, by David Masters, Henry Holt and Company, Incorporated, New York, 1934.

Air, Men, and Wings, by Lloyd George and James Gilman, The McBride Company, Inc., New York, 1929.

Heroes of the Air, by Chelsea Fraser, Thomas Y. Crowell Company, New York, 1942.

This Flying Game, by Brigadier General H. H. Arnold, Funk & Wagnalls Company, New York, 1936.

BIBLIOGRAPHY

Heroes of the Air, revised by Martha Wood, Thomas Y. Crowell Company, New York, 1946.

The Romance of Aeronautics, by Charles C. Turner, J. B. Lippincott Company, London, 1912.

Wings Away, by James Elliott Mooney, Thomas Nelson & Sons, New York, 1946.

The Book of Gliders, by Edwin Way Teale, E. P. Dutton & Co., Inc., New York, 1930.

The Conquest of the Air, by Alphonse Berget, G. P. Putnam's Sons, New York, 1911.

The Airman's Almanac, edited by Francis Walton, Rinehart & Company, Inc., New York, 1945.

Man's Fight to Fly, by John P. V. Heinmuller, Funk & Wagnalls Company, New York, 1944.

The Story of American Aviation, by Jim Ray, John C. Winston Company, Philadelphia, 1946.

Meet the Parachute, by O. J. Mink, Reliance Manufacturing Co., Chicago, 1944.

Gliders and Glider Training, by Emanuele Stieri, Essential Books, dist. by Duell, Sloan & Pearce, Inc., New York, 1943.

Everyman's Book of Flying, by Orville H. Kneen, Frederick A. Stokes Co., New York, 1930.

Romance of the Airman, by Pauline A. Humphreys, Ginn and Company, Boston, 1931.

Historic Airships, by Rupert Sargent Holland, Macrae Smith Company, Philadelphia, 1928.

Horizons Unlimited, by Samuel Paul Johnston, Duell, Sloan & Pearce, Inc., New York, 1941.

The First Air Voyage in America, by Jean Pierre Blanchard, Penn Mutual Life Insurance Company, Philadelphia, 1943.

FROM KITE TO KITTY HAWK

The Romance of Aircraft, by Lawrence Yard Smith, Frederick A. Stokes Company, New York, 1919.

Parachutes, by Herbert S. Zim, Harcourt, Brace & Company, New York, 1942.

My Air-Ships, by A. Santos-Dumont, The Century Co., New York, 1904.

Knights of the Air, by Lt. Lester J. Maitland, Doubleday & Company, Inc., Garden City, New York, 1929.

The Wonder Book of Aircraft, edited by Harry Golding, F.R.G.S., Ward Lock & Co., Ltd., London, 1930.

Sky High, The Story of Aviation, by Eric Hodgins and F. Alexander Magoun, Little, Brown and Company, Boston, 1930.

The Story of Aircraft, by Chelsea Fraser, Thomas Y. Crowell Company, New York, 1933, 1939 editions.

Riding the Air, by Dorothy Judd Sickels, American Book Company, New York, 1943.

The Wonder Book of the Air, by C. B. Allen and Lauren D. Lyman, The Junior Literary Guild and John C. Winston Company, Philadelphia, 1936.

The World Almanac and Book of Facts for 1954, edited by Harry Hansen, New York World-Telegram and Sun, New York, 1954.

Facts on File, Facts on File, Inc., 516 Fifth Avenue, New York, New York, 1954-5-6.

Flight, Today & Tomorrow, by Margaret O. Hyde, McGraw-Hill Book Company, Inc., New York, 1953.

A Flier's World, by Wolfgang Langewiesche, McGraw-Hill Book Company, Inc., New York, 1951.

Test Pilot, by Neville Duke, Allan Wingate, London, 1954.

A History of Flying, by C. H. Gibbs-Smith, B. T. Batsford, Ltd., London, 1953.

Index

INDEX

207

INDEX

INDEX

ABOUT THE AUTHOR

Richard W. Bishop was born in Medford, Massachusetts. Following in his lawyer-father's footsteps, he was graduated from Boston University, School of Law.

During World War II, Mr. Bishop served as an officer with the Judge Advocate General's Department of the Army. He now lives in a suburb of Boston where he is active in the Bar Associations and Rotary Club.

Mr. Bishop has written stories and articles on many subjects: legal photography, hobbies, historical and present-day characters. He has published two books for young people, *Stepping Stones to Light* and *From Kite to Kitty Hawk*.